Measuring Up®

to the

New York State Learning Standards

and Success Strategies for the State Test

Mathematics

This book is customized for New York and the lessons match the
New York State Learning Standards—Mathematics. The Measuring Up®
program includes comprehensive worktexts and New York
Diagnostic Practice Tests, which are available separately.

Level
H

800-822-1080
www.PeoplesEducation.com

Peoples Education®
Your partner in student success™

Executive Vice President and Chief Creative Officer: Diane Miller

Vice President, Product Development: Steven Jay Griffel

Editorial Development: ELHI Publisher Services

Editorial Direction and Production: Victory Productions

Assistant Vice President, Editorial Director: Eugene McCormick

Director of Editorial Services: Lee Shenkman

Vice President of Marketing: Victoria Ameer Kiely

Director of Marketing: Melissa Dubno Geller

Vice President of Production and Manufacturing: Doreen Smith

Production Director: Nicole Dawson

Project Manager: Tara Bernstein

Designer: Jodi Notowitz

Technical Art: Armando Báez, Tara Bernstein, Sal Esposito, Shani Hawkins, Matthew Hjembo, Sharon MacGregor, Michelle Sloane, Tracy Wilhelmy

Cover Design: Cynthia Mackowicz, Michele Sakow, Yadiro Henriquez

New York Advisory Panel, Elementary

Harriet Notowitz
Educator
(Math/Literacy)

Sandy H. Ehrlich
Assistant Principal
I.S. 109Q

Peoples Education®
Your partner in student success™

Copyright © 2006
Peoples Education, Inc.
299 Market Street
Saddle Brook, New Jersey 07663

ISBN 978-1-4138-2321-9

Printed in the United States of America.

10 9 8 7 6 5

Measuring Up® Contents

Chapter 1   Number Sense and Operations

Performance Indicators	Lesson	
8.N.1, 8.PS.1	**1**	The Laws of Exponents for Multiplication and Division 2
8.N.2, 8.RP.2, 8.RP.7	**2**	Evaluate Expressions with Exponents 4
8.N.3, 8.CN.2	**3**	Percents Less than 1% or Greater than 100% 6
8.N.4, 8.PS.14, 8.CN.3	**4**	Applying Percents 8
8.N.5, 8.R.10	**5**	Estimate a Percent 10
8.N.6, 8.CN.7	**6**	Justify the Reasonableness of Answers Using Estimation . . 12

Chapter 1   Number Sense and Operations *(continued)*

Chapter 2   Algebra

Chapter 2   Algebra *(continued)*

Chapter 3   Geometry

Chapter 3   Geometry *(continued)*

Chapter 4   Measurement

Grade 7   Post-March Standards Review

Student Resources

For a quick review of concepts, review the glossary of terms. If you are having difficulty with a concept, review that lesson again.

DPTs (Diagnostic Practice Tests) . . . . Measuring Up® Supplement

Your teacher may choose to give Diagnostic Practice Tests that assess your understanding of mathematics skills and concepts that come from your New York State Learning Standards. This will help you focus on areas where you need some extra help.

Lesson Correlation to the New York State Learning Standards

This worktext is 100% customized to the New York State Learning Standards and will help you prepare for the *New York State Test*!

New York State Learning Standards for Mathematics	Measuring Up® Lessons
Content Strand: Number Sense and Operations	
Operations: Students will understand meanings of operations and procedures, and how they relate to one another.	
8.N.1 Develop and apply the laws of exponents for multiplication and division	1; 16
8.N.2 Evaluate expressions with integral exponents	2
8.N.3 Read, write, and identify percents less than 1% and greater than 100%	3
8.N.4 Apply percents to: tax, percent increase/decrease, simple interest, sale price, commission, interest rates, gratuities	4; 7
Estimation: Students will compute accurately and make reasonable estimates.	
8.N.5 Estimate a percent of quantity, given an application	5
8.N.6 Justify the reasonableness of answers using estimation	6; 9; 10
Content Strand: Algebra	
Variables and Expressions: Students will represent and analyze algebraically a wide variety of problem solving situations.	
8.A.1 Translate verbal sentences into algebraic inequalities	12
8.A.2 Write verbal expressions that match given mathematical expressions	12
8.A.3 Describe a situation involving relationships that matches a given graph	13
8.A.4 Create a graph given a description or an expression for a situation involving a linear or nonlinear relationship	14
8.A.5 Use physical models to perform operations with polynomials	15
Variables and Expressions: Students will perform algebraic procedures accurately.	
8.A.6 Multiply and divide monomials	16
8.A.7 Add and subtract polynomials (integer coefficients)	17
8.A.8 Multiply a binomial by a monomial or a binomial (integer coefficients)	18
8.A.9 Divide a polynomial by a monomial (integer coefficients). Note: The degree of the denominator is less than or equal to the degree of the numerator for all variables.	19
8.A.10 Factor algebraic expressions using the GCF	20
8.A.11 Factor a trinomial in the form $ax^2 + bx + c$; a=1 and c having no more than three sets of factors	21
Equations and Inequalities:	
8.A.12 Apply algebra to determine the measure of angles formed by or contained in parallel lines cut by a transversal and by intersecting lines	22
8.A.13 Solve multi-step inequalities and graph the solution set on a number line	23
8.A.14 Solve linear inequalities by combining like terms, using the distributive property, or moving variables to one side of the inequality (include multiplication or division of inequalities by a negative number	24
Patterns, Relations, and Functions: Students will recognize, use, and represent algebraically patterns, relations, and functions.	
8.A.15 Understand that numerical information can be represented in multiple ways: arithmetically, algebraically, and graphically	25; 30; 32; 33

continued

New York State Learning Standards for Mathematics		Measuring Up® Lessons
8.A.16	Find a set of ordered pairs to satisfy a given linear numerical pattern (expressed algebraically); then plot the ordered pairs and draw the line	14
8.A.17	Define and use correct terminology when referring to function (domain and range)	26; 29; 31
8.A.18	Determine if a relation is a function	27
8.A.19	Interpret multiple representations using equation, table of values, and graph	28
Content Strand: Geometry		
Constructions: Students will use visualization and spatial reasoning to analyze characteristics and properties of geometric shapes.		
8.G.0	Construct the following, using a straight edge and compass: segment congruent to a segment, angle congruent to an angle, perpendicular bisector, angle bisector	34
Geometric Relationships: Students will identify and justify geometric relationships, formally and informally.		
8.G.1	Identify pairs of vertical angles as congruent	35
8.G.2	Identify pairs of supplementary and complementary angles	36
8.G.3	Calculate the missing angle in a supplementary or complementary pair	37; 55
8.G.4	Determine angle pair relationships when given two parallel lines cut by a transversal	38
8.G.5	Calculate the missing angle measurements when given two parallel lines cut by a transversal	39
8.G.6	Calculate the missing angle measurements when given two intersecting lines and an angle	40
Transformational Geometry: Students will apply transformations and symmetry to analyze problem solving situations,		
8.G.7	Describe and identify transformations in the plane, using proper function notation (rotations, reflections, translations, and dilations)	41
8.G.8	Draw the image of a figure under rotations of 90 and 180 degrees	42
8.G.9	Draw the image of a figure under a reflection over a given line	43
8.G.10	Draw the image of a figure under a translation	43; 57
8.G.11	Draw the image of a figure under a dilation	43
8.G.12	Identify the properties preserved and not preserved under a reflection, rotation, translation, and dilation	44
Coordinate Geometry: Students will apply coordinate geometry to analyze problem solving situations.		
8.G.13	Determine the slope of a line from a graph and explain the meaning of slope as a constant rate of change	45; 57; 58
8.G.14	Determine the y-intercept of a line from a graph and be able to explain the y-intercept	46
8.G.15	Graph a line using a table of values	47
8.G.16	Determine the equation of a line given the slope and the y-intercept	48
8.G.17	Graph a line from an equation in slope-intercept form ( )	49; 54
8.G.18	Solve systems of equations graphically (only linear, integral solutions, format, no vertical/horizontal lines)	50
8.G.19	Graph the solution set of an inequality on a number line	51
8.G.20	Distinguish between linear and nonlinear equations $ax^2 + bx + c$; a=1 (only graphically)	52
8.G.21	Recognize the characteristics of quadratics in tables, graphs, equations, and situations	53

continued

New York State Learning Standards for Mathematics		Measuring Up® Lessons
Content Strand: Measurement		
Units of Measurement: Students will determine what can be measured and how, using appropriate methods and formulas.		
8.M.1	Solve equations/proportions to convert to equivalent measurements Note: also allow Fahrenheit to Celsius and vice versa.	59; 60; 61; 62; 63; 64
Process Strand: Problem Solving		
Students will build new mathematical knowledge through problem solving.		
8.PS.1	Use a variety of strategies to understand new mathematical content and to develop more efficient methods	1; 7
8.PS.2	Construct appropriate extentions to problem situations	28
8.PS.3	Understand and demonstrate how written symbols represent mathematical ideas	24
Students will solve problems that arise in mathematics and other contexts		
8.PS.4	Observe patterns and formulate generalizations	40; 53
8.PS.5	Make conjectures from generalizations	38
8.PS.6	Represent problem situations verbally, numerically, algebraically, and graphically	45
Students will apply and adapt a variety of appropriate strategies to solve problems.		
8.PS.7	Understand that there is no one right way to solve mathematical problems but that different methods have advantages and disadvantages	28
8.PS.8	Understand how to break a complex problem into simpler parts or use a similar problem type to solve a problem	54
8.PS.9	Work backwards from a solution	8
8.PS.10	Use proportionality to model problems	56; 59; 60
8.PS.11	Work in collaboration with others to solve problems	Under teacher direction and observation
Students will monitor and reflect on the process of mathematical problem solving.		
8.PS.12	Interpret solutions within the given constraints of a problem	29; 51
8.PS.13	Set expectations and limits for possible solutions	12; 29
8.PS.14	Determine information required to solve the problem	4
8.PS.15	Choose methods for obtaining required information	63
8.PS.16	Justify solution methods through logical argument	8
8.PS.17	Evaluate the efficiency of different representations of a problem	28
Process Strand: Reasoning and Proof		
Students will recognize reasoning and proof as fundamental aspects of mathematics.		
8.RP.1	Recognize that mathematical ideas can be supported by a variety of strategies	28
Students will make and investigate mathematical conjectures.		
8.RP.2	Use mathematical strategies to reach a conclusion	2; 8; 24; 39; 51; 55
8.RP.3	Investigate conjectures, using arguments and appropriate mathematical terms	35
Students will develop and evaluate mathematical arguments and proofs.		
8.RP.4	Provide supportive arguments for conjectures	36; 55
8.RP.5	Develop, verify, and explain an argument, using appropriate mathematical ideas and language	30

continued

New York State Learning Standards for Mathematics		Measuring Up® Lessons
Students will select and use various types of reasoning and methods of proof.		
8.RP.6	Support an argument by using a systematic approach to test more than one case	61
8.RP.7	Devise ways to verify results or use counterexamples to refute incorrect statements	2
8.RP.8	Apply inductive reasoning in making and supporting mathematical conjectures	22; 37
Process Strand: Communication		
Students will organize and consolidate their mathematical thinking through communication.		
8.CM.1	Provide a correct, complete, coherent, and clear rationale for thought process used in problem solving	18
8.CM.2	Provide an organized argument which explains rationale for strategy selection	61; 62
8.CM.3	Organize and accurately label work	27
Students will communicate their mathematical thinking coherently and clearly to peers, teachers, and others.		
8.CM.4	Share organized mathematical ideas through the manipulation of objects, numerical tables, drawings, pictures, charts, graphs, tables, diagrams, models and symbols in written and verbal form	26; 41; 62
8.CM.5	Answer clarifying questions from others	Under teacher direction and observation
Students will analyze and evaluate the mathematical thinking and strategies of others.		
8.CM.6	Analyze mathematical solutions shared by others	Under teacher direction and observation
8.CM.7	Compare strategies used and solutions found by others in relation to their own work	9
8.CM.8	Formulate mathematical questions that elicit, extend, or challenge strategies, solutions, and/or conjectures of others	Under teacher direction and observation
Students will use the language of mathematics to express mathematical ideas precisely.		
8.CM.9	Increase their use of mathematical vocabulary and language when communicating with others	Under teacher direction and observation
8.CM.10	Use appropriate language, representations, and terminology when describing objects, relationships, mathematical solutions, and rationale	13; 31; 36; 42; 50; 56
8.CM.11	Draw conclusions about mathematical ideas through decoding, comprehension, and interpretation of mathematical visuals, symbols, and technical writing	19
Process Strand: Connections		
Students will recognize and use connections among mathematical ideas.		
8.CN.1	Understand and make connections among multiple representations of the same mathematical idea	14; 16; 32; 44
8.CN.2	Recognize connections between subsets of mathematical ideas	3; 17; 27; 49; 57
8.CN.3	Connect and apply a variety of strategies to solve problems	4
Students will understand how mathematical ideas interconnect and build on one another to produce a coherent whole.		
8.CN.4	Model situations mathematically, using representations to draw conclusions and formulate new situations	8; 21; 46; 48
8.CN.5	Understand how concepts, procedures, and mathematical results in one area of mathematics can be used to solve problems in other areas of mathematics	10
Students will recognize and apply mathematics in contexts outside of mathematics.		
8.CN.6	Recognize and provide examples of the presence of mathematics in their daily lives	63
8.CN.7	Apply mathematics to problem situations that develop outside of mathematics	6; 59
8.CN.8	Investigate the presence of mathematics in careers and areas of interest	56
8.CN.9	Recognize and apply mathematics to other disciplines and areas of interest, and societal issues	59

continued

New York State Learning Standards for Mathematics	Measuring Up® Lessons
Process Strand: Representation	
Students will create and use representations to organize, record, and communicate mathematical ideas.	
8.R.1 Use physical objects, drawings, charts, tables, graphs, symbols, equations, or objects created using technology as representations	11; 15
8.R.2 Explain, describe, and defend mathematical ideas using representations	34; 52
8.R.3 Recognize, compare, and use an array of representational forms	38
8.R.4 Explain how different representations express the same relationship	25
8.R.5 Use standard and non-standard representations with accuracy and detail	32; 33; 42; 43
Students will select, apply, and translate among mathematical representations to solve problems.	
8.R.6 Use representations to explore problem situations	12; 25
8.R.7 Investigate relationships between different representations and their impact on a given problem	28
8.R.8 Use representation as a tool for exploring and understanding mathematical ideas	11; 20; 23; 33; 35; 36; 43; 47; 58
Students will use representations to model and interpret physical, social, and mathematical phenomena.	
8.R.9 Use mathematics to show and understand mathematical phenomena (e.g., make and interpret scale drawings of figures or scale models of objects)	56; 64
8.R.10 Use mathematics to show and understand social phenomena (e.g., determine profit from sale of yearbooks)	5
8.R.11 Use mathematics to show and understand mathematical phenomena (e.g., use tables, graphs, and equations to show a pattern underlying a function)	27

Letter to Students

Dear Student,

How do you get better at anything you do? You practice! Just like with sports or other activities, the way to success in school is practice, practice, practice.

This book will help you review and practice mathematics strategies and skills. These are the strategies and skills you need to know to measure up to the New York State Learning Standards in Mathematics for your grade. Practicing these skills and strategies now will help you do better in your work all year. Your skills practice will also help you score high on the *New York State Test* for Mathematics, as well as on other mathematics tests that you will take this school year.

This book has four chapters: Number Sense and Operations; Algebra; Geometry; and Measurement. Each lesson has three main sections:

Think About It, which presents a problem or idea that will get you started thinking about the math covered in the lesson;

Here's How, which shows you the steps and skills necessary to solve problems;

Practice, which helps you practice important concepts and skills reviewed in the lesson.

This book gives you lots of chances to practice multiple-choice and short- and extended-response problems like the ones you will see on the Grade 8 *New York State Test*. The *Practice Test* sections at the end of each chapter include more difficult questions that will help sharpen your higher-level thinking skills.

Also, a Grade 7 Post-March Standards Review section is located at the end of the book and will help you review mathematics skills that you learned in Grade 7, but that you may be tested on this year.

This school year you will take the *New York State Test*. It will be an important step forward. The test will show how well you measure up to the New York State Learning Standards for Mathematics. It is just one of the many important tests you will take.

Have a great year!

Letter to Parents and Families

Dear Parents and Families,

All students need mathematics skills to succeed. New York educators have created grade-appropriate standards called the New York State Learning Standards for Mathematics. The New York State Learning Standards describe what all New York students should know at each grade level. Students need to meet these standards, as measured by the *New York State Test*, which your child will take this school year.

Measuring Up® is 100% customized to the New York State Learning Standards for Mathematics for Grade 8. These standards emphasize higher-level thinking skills students must learn to analyze, interpret, and generalize, as well as recall facts and operate with numbers. This book will help your child review the skills and concepts described in the standards and prepare for the *New York State Test* and other Grade 8 mathematics tests. It contains:

- **Lessons** that focus on practicing the skills described in the New York State Learning Standards;
- **Think About It**, which presents a problem or idea that will get students started thinking about the mathematics covered in the lesson;
- **Here's How**, which shows students the steps and skills necessary to solve problems;
- **Practice**, which helps students practice important concepts and skills reviewed in the lesson. It shows students how individual standards can be understood through answering multiple-choice and short- and extended-response questions similar to those on the *New York State Test*;
- **Grade 7 Post-March Standards Review**, which reviews skills from the prior grade level that may appear on the Grade 8 *New York State Test* for Mathematics.

For success in school and in the real world, your child needs to be successful in mathematics. Get involved! Your involvement is crucial to your child's success. Here are some suggestions:

- Keep mathematics alive in your home. Involve your child in activities that use mathematics, such as mixing recipes, counting coins, telling time, and identifying geometric shapes and patterns.
- Look for ways mathematics is used when you are out with your family. Encourage your child to count your change after making a purchase, read the items and prices in a restaurant menu, identify shapes such as spheres and cubes in real objects, and add or subtract to find how many there are or how many are left in real-life situations.
- Ask your child to talk and write about what they have learned in mathematics. Always encourage them to use mathematical language.
- Encourage your child to take the time to review and check his or her homework. Finding a solution is just one part of solving a problem. Ask your child to tell why his or her answers are reasonable and make sense.

Work with us this year to ensure your child's success. Mathematics is essential not only for success in school, but in the world as well.

This book was created for New York students just like you. Each lesson and question is aimed at helping you master the New York State Learning Standards for Mathematics and do well on the *New York State Test* in Mathematics for Grade 8. It will also help you do well on other mathematics exams you take during the school year.

About the Test
New York educators have set up standards for mathematics. They are called the New York State Learning Standards and Core Curriculum. These standards spell out what students at each grade level should know. New York educators have also created a statewide test for mathematics, which you will take this March. It is called the Grade 8 *New York State Test* for Mathematics. It shows how well students have mastered the learning standards. Test questions go along with and meet the Grade 7 Post-March and Grade 8 Pre-March test related Performance Indicators from the following Content Strands within the New York State Learning Standards for Mathematics:

The Four Content Strands:
Number Sense and Operations Strand
Algebra Strand
Geometry Strand
Measurement Strand

The New York State Learning Standards and Core Curriculum also include the following Process Strands, which are meant to be integrated throughout all mathematics concepts taught during the school year.

The Five Process Strands:
Problem Solving Strand
Reasoning and Proof Strand
Communication Strand
Connections Strand
Representation Strand

Format of the Test
The Grade 8 *New York State Test* for Mathematics is given in March and is broken up into three sessions. You will see many question types on the *New York State Test* such as multiple-choice, short-response, and extended-response questions.

Session 1 of the *New York State Test* for Mathematics includes 27 multiple-choice questions, which you will have 45 minutes to complete. Session 2 has 4 short-response questions and 2 extended-response questions that you will have 35 minutes to answer. Session 3 has 8 short-response questions and 4 extended-response questions that you will have 65 minutes to complete.

Many questions include a picture, a graph, a number line, or another type of graphic that is used to solve the problem. This book gives you practice in reading and using these types of graphics.

Measuring Up® **on Multiple-Choice Questions**

A multiple-choice question has two parts. The first part is the stem, or question. It has a number in front of it. The second part is made up of the answer choices. Each answer choice has a letter in front of it. You will be asked to read each question and then circle the letter for the best answer.

Some of the multiple-choice questions have a graph or table. You will need to read information from the graph or table to solve the problem.

For example, in the question below, you will need to read the information in the table, select the answer choice that seems most reasonable, then circle the letter next to that answer.

1 The table below shows the cost of flowers in a flower shop.

Number of Flowers	Cost
4	$1.00
5	$1.25
6	$1.50
7	$1.75

How much does one flower cost?

A 10 cents   **Ⓒ** 25 cents

B 20 cents   **D** 50 cents

By studying the pattern in the table, you can see that each flower costs 25 cents. So C is the correct answer. Notice how to mark your answer.

Here are some strategies for answering multiple-choice questions:

- Try to work the problem without looking at the answer choices. Once you have solved the problem, compare your answer with the answer choices.

- Eliminate answer choices you know are wrong. Then choose from the answers that are left.

- Some questions will be more difficult than others. The problem may require an extra step, or you may need to look for which answers do not apply.

- Even if you don't know the answer, you can make a good guess based on what you know and get the right answer.

- Check and double-check your answers before you turn in the test. Be sure of your answers.

Measuring Up® **on Short-Response Questions**

Short-response questions have blanks that you need to fill in with the correct answer. Be sure to write your answer carefully and neatly.

Measuring Up® **on Extended-Response Questions**

Extended-response questions have blanks that you will need to fill in with the correct answer. There is also a place for you to write and explain your answer.

Here are some tips for answering extended-response questions:
- Carefully work the problem. You do not have answer choices as a way to check your work. Use your time wisely and follow all the steps carefully.
- When you have an answer, carefully write it down.
- Use information from the problem and your answer to help you write an explanation of your work and reasoning. Show all of your thinking.
- Read over your explanation. Does it say what you wanted to explain?

Higher-Level Thinking Skills

Higher-level thinking skills are important on the *New York State Test.* When you use higher-level thinking skills, you do more than just recall information. On the *New York State Test*, some questions ask you to find and continue a pattern, understand and use information in a table or graph, or use a number line. Instead of adding or subtracting to solve a problem, you may need to solve a two-step problem and use both operations.

Measuring Up® **with Grade 7 Post-March Standards Review**

Measuring Up® includes a section at the back of the book called Grade 7 Post-March Standards Review. This section will help you review mathematics skills that you learned in Grade 7, but may appear on the Grade 8 *New York State Test* that you will have to take this year.

Tips for Measuring Up®

Here are some more test-taking tips for you to keep in mind. These tips will help you do better on the tests you will take this year.
- Start getting ready now. Spend a few minutes a day answering practice test questions.
- Get a good night's sleep the night before the test.
- Eat a good breakfast.
- Keep telling yourself that you will do well. Then you probably will. That's what it means to "think positively."

You will learn a lot in Measuring Up®. You will review and practice the skills included in the New York State Learning Standards. You will practice for the Grade 8 *New York State Test* for Mathematics. Finally, you will build stamina to answer tough questions. You will more than measure up. You will be a smashing success!

Rubric for Short-Response Questions

2 Points   A two-point response is complete and correct.

This response
- demonstrates a thorough understanding of the mathematical concepts and/or procedures embodied in the task

- indicates that the student has completed the task correctly, using mathematically sound procedures

- contains clear, complete explanations and/or adequate work when required

1 Point   A one-point response is only partially correct.

This response
- indicates that the student has demonstrated only a partial understanding of the mathematical concepts and/or procedures embodied in the task

- may contain an incorrect solution but applies a mathematically appropriate process

- may contain a correct numerical answer but required work is not provided

0 Points   A zero-point response is completely incorrect, irrelevant, or incoherent, or a correct response arrived at using an obviously incorrect procedure.

Rubric for Extended-Response Questions

3 Points   A three-point response is complete and correct.

This response
- demonstrates a thorough understanding of the mathematical concepts and/or procedures embodied in the task

- indicates that the student has completed the task correctly, using mathematically sound procedures

- contains clear, complete explanations and/or adequate work when required

2 Points   A two-point response is partially correct.

This response
- demonstrates partial understanding of the mathematical concepts and/or procedures embodied in the task

- addresses most aspects of the task, using mathematically sound procedures

- may contain a correct solution but provides incomplete procedures, reasoning, and/or explanations

- may reflect some misunderstanding of the underlying mathematical concepts and/or procedures

1 Point   A one-point response is incomplete and exhibits many flaws but is not completely incorrect.

This response
- demonstrates only a limited understanding of the mathematical concepts and/or procedures embodied in the task

- may address some elements of the task correctly but reaches an inadequate solution and/or provides reasoning that is faulty or incomplete

- exhibits multiple flaws related to a misunderstanding of important aspects of the task, misuse of mathematical procedures, or faulty mathematical reasoning

- reflects a lack of essential understanding of the underlying mathematical concepts

- may contain a correct numerical answer but required work is not provided

0 Points   A zero-point response is completely incorrect, irrelevant, or incoherent, or a correct response arrived at using an obviously incorrect procedure.

Performance indicators: **8.N.1, 8.PS.1**

READY REFERENCE

exponent a number that expresses how many times a base is used as a factor; *example:* in the expression 6^4, the exponent is 4

base the number in an expression that is used as a factor; *example:* in the expression 6^4, 6 is the base.

Think About It

How can you simplify exponent expressions? The laws of exponents for multiplication and division assume that the bases are equal. The base in the following equations is x.

$$x^5 \bullet x^2 = x^?$$
$$x^5 \div x^2 = x^?$$

Here's How

Add exponents when multiplying.

Step 1 Convert each expression with an exponent into a multiplication expression.

$$x^5 \bullet x^2 = (x \bullet x \bullet x \bullet x \bullet x) \times (x \bullet x)$$

Step 2 Simplify using the Associative Property.

$$x^5 \bullet x^2 = (x \bullet x \bullet x \bullet x \bullet x) \bullet (x \bullet x) = (x \bullet x \bullet x \bullet x \bullet x \bullet x \bullet x)$$

Step 3 Convert the resulting expression into an expression with an exponent.

$$x^5 \bullet x^2 = x \bullet x \bullet x \bullet x \bullet x \bullet x \bullet x = \underline{\hspace{1.5cm}}$$

Step 4 The law of exponents for multiplication is:

$$x^m \bullet x^n = x^{m+n}$$

Subtract exponents when dividing.

Step 1 Write the division as a fraction.

$$x^5 \div x^2 = \frac{x^5}{x^2}$$

Step 2 Convert each expression with an exponent into a multiplication expression.

$$x^5 \div x^2 = \frac{x^5}{x^2} = \frac{x \bullet x \bullet x \bullet x \bullet x}{x \bullet x}$$

Step 3 Simplify and convert the resulting expression into an expression with an exponent.

$$x^5 \div x^2 = \frac{x^5}{x^2} = \frac{x \bullet x \bullet x \bullet \cancel{x} \bullet \cancel{x}}{\cancel{x} \bullet \cancel{x}} = x \bullet x \bullet x = \underline{\hspace{1.5cm}}$$

Step 4 The law of exponents for division is:

$$x^m \div x^n = x^{m-n}$$

🔑 Practice

1 What is the exponent x in the equation $3^5 \cdot 3^3 = 3^x$?

A 15

B 8

C 2

D 1.67

2 What is the exponent x in the equation $3^5 \div 3^3 = 3^x$?

F 1.67

G 2

H 8

J 15

3 What is the exponent x in the equation $1.78^4 \cdot 1.78^6 = 1.78^x$?

A 24

B 10

C 1.5

D −2

4 What is the exponent x in the equation $1.78^a \div 1.78^b = 1.78^x$?

F $a \div b$

G $a + b$

H $a \cdot b$

J $a - b$

5 What is the exponent x in the equation $12^p \cdot 12^q = 12^x$?

A $p \div q$

B $p + q$

C $p \cdot q$

D $p - q$

6 What is the exponent x in the equation $12^6 \div 12^4 = 12^x$?

F −2

G 2

H 10

J 24

7 What is the exponent x in the equation $9^5 \cdot 9^{-2} = 9^x$?

A −10

B −3

C 3

D 7

8 What is the exponent x in the equation $9^5 \div 9^{-2} = 9^x$?

F −10

G −3

H 3

J 7

Short-Response Question

9 Express the following with exponents and then simplify.

$(4 \cdot 4 \cdot 4 \cdot 4 \cdot 4) \cdot (4 \cdot 4 \cdot 4 \cdot 4 \cdot 4 \cdot 4 \cdot 4)$

_____

_____

Performance indicators: **8.N.2, 8.RP.2, 8.RP.7**

READY REFERENCE

power   any expression written in exponential form, such as 3^2 or a^3

base   the number in an expression that is used as a factor; in the expression 3^2, 3 is base

exponent   a number that expresses how many times a base is used as a factor; *example:* in the expresion 6^4, 4 is the exponent

zero as an exponent   for any non-zero number a, $a^0 = 1$

🔑 Think About It

How do you simplify expressions with exponents? You know that $\frac{5}{5} = 1$. Would $\frac{5^2}{5^2} = 1$? Take this idea a step further. You have learned that $\frac{5^2}{5^2} = 5^{(2-2)}$. What is the value of 5^0?

🔑 Here's How

Zero as an Exponent

Subtract the exponents to divide numbers with the same base.

$$\frac{5^2}{5^2} = 5^{(2-2)}$$ What is the value of the exponent? _____

$$\frac{5^2}{5^2} = \frac{\cancel{5} \times \cancel{5}}{\cancel{5} \times \cancel{5}} = \frac{1}{1} = 1$$

Evaluate $\frac{6^5}{6^5}$

To evaluate this fraction, subtract the exponents.

$$\frac{6^5}{6^5} = 6^{5-5} = 6^0 = 1$$

$$\frac{6^5}{6^5} = 6^{5-5} = 6^0 = 1$$

The square of any non-zero integer is a positive number.

$(-3)^2 = -3 \bullet (-3) = $ ____

What is the sign of a product of two numbers with the same sign? ____

What is the value $(-3)^2$?

Evaluate $20 - 5^2$.

Recall that the order of operations states that exponents must be evaluated before subtracting.

What is 5^2? ____

What is $20 - 5^2$? ____

Practice

1 Evaluate $5^3 \cdot 5^2$.

   A $5^6 = 15{,}625$ **C** $5^2 = 25$

   B $5^5 = 3{,}125$ **D** $5^1 = 5$

2 Evaluate $5^5 \div 5$.

   F $5^4 = 625$ **H** $5^6 = 15{,}625$

   G $5^5 = 3{,}225$ **J** $5^7 = 78{,}125$

3 Evaluate $2^4 \cdot 2^2$.

   A $2^0 = 1$ **C** $2^6 = 64$

   B $2^2 = 4$ **D** $2^{16} = 65{,}536$

4 Evaluate $2^4 \div 2^4$.

   F $2^0 = 1$ **H** $2^8 = 256$

   G $2^1 = 2$ **J** $2^{16} = 65{,}536$

5 Evaluate $3^3 \cdot 3^1$.

   A $3^2 = 9$ **C** $3^4 = 81$

   B $3^3 = 27$ **D** $4^3 = 64$

6 Evaluate $3^3 \div 3^1$.

   F $3^4 = 81$ **H** $3^2 = 9$

   G $3^3 = 27$ **J** $3^1 = 3$

7 Evaluate $4^4 \cdot 4^{-2}$.

   A $4^{-2} = \frac{1}{4^2}$ **C** $4^4 = 256$

   B $4^2 = 16$ **D** $4^6 = 4{,}096$

8 Evaluate $4^4 \div 4^{-2}$.

   F $4^{-2} = \frac{1}{4^2}$ **H** $4^4 = 256$

   G $4^2 = 16$ **J** $4^6 = 4{,}096$

9 Evaluate $(-7)^2$.

   A -49 **C** 14

   B -14 **D** 49

10 Evaluate $(5-6)^2$.

   F -5 **H** 1

   G -1 **J** 25

11 Evaluate $10 \cdot (-10)^2$.

   A $-1{,}000$ **C** -10

   B -100 **D** $1{,}000$

12 Evaluate $(-7)^2 - 8^2$.

   F -79 **H** 15

   G -15 **J** 57

13 Evaluate $\frac{8^4}{8^4}$.

   A 0 **C** $4{,}096$

   B 1 **D** $16{,}777{,}216$

14 Evaluate $10^2 \cdot \frac{10^2}{10^2}$.

   F $10{,}000$ **H** 100

   G $1{,}000$ **J** 1

Short-Response Question

15 Tell whether each statement is true or false. If a statement is false, explain why.

$2^2 \cdot 2^2 = 2^{2+2} = 16$ _____

$10^2 \div 10^1 = 10^1 = 10$ _____

$3^8 \div 3^4 = 3^{12} = 531{,}441$ _____

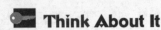

Performance indicators: **8.N.3, 8.CN.2**

 **Think About It**

How do you convert fractions and decimals to percents less than 1% or greater than 100%?

Here's How

Convert $\frac{3}{2}$ to a percent.

Step 1 First convert the fraction to an equivalent fraction with a denominator of 100.

$$\frac{3}{2} \times \frac{50}{50} = \frac{150}{100}$$

Step 2 Write the fraction as a percent.

$\frac{150}{100} =$ _____ Read this as one hundred fifty percent.

Convert 0.0032 to a percent.

Step 1 Convert the decimal to a fraction with a denominator of 100.

$$0.0032 \times \frac{100}{100} =$$ _____

Step 2 Write the fraction as a percent.

$\frac{0.32}{100} =$ _____ Read this as thirty-two hundredths percent.

Convert 0.25% to a fraction.

Step 1 Write 0.25% as a fraction with a denominator of 100.

$$0.25\% = \frac{0.25}{100}$$

Step 2 Multiply the numerator and denominator by the same factor to eliminate the decimal in the numerator. If necessary, reduce to simplest terms.

$$\frac{0.25}{100} \times \frac{4}{4} =$$ _____

Convert 122.6% to a decimal.

Step 1 First write 122.6% as a fraction with a denominator of 100.

$$122.6\% = \frac{122.6}{100}$$

Step 2 Rewrite as a division.

$$\frac{122.6}{100} = 122.6 \div 100$$

Step 3 Divide and write as a decimal. $122.6 \div 100 =$ _____

🔑 Practice

1 How do you write 143% as a decimal?

A 14.3

B 1.43

C 0.143

D 0.0143

2 How do you write 0.72% as a decimal?

F 7.2

G 0.72

H 0.072

J 0.0072

3 How do you write 0.003 as a percent?

A 30%

B 3%

C 0.3%

D 0.03%

4 How do you write 23.82 as a percent?

F 2,382%

G 238.2%

H 23.82%

J 2.382%

5 What is 125% of 52?

A 650

B 65

C 6.5

D 0.65

6 What is 0.4% of 780?

F 312

G 31.2

H 3.12

J 0.312

Short-Response Question

7 Last year, the Hilltopper Race raised a total of $3,400 for cancer research. This year's race raised 137% of last year's total. Did this year's race meet the organizers' goal of $4,500? If so, by how much money? Show all work.

_____

_____

Performance indicators: **8.N.4, 8.PS.14, 8.CN.3**

> **READY REFERENCE**
>
> **percent of change** the ratio of the amount of change to the original amount;
>
> $P = \dfrac{\text{amount of change}}{\text{original amount}}$
>
> **rate** a ratio comparing two different types of quantities, such as miles to gallons or feet to seconds
>
> **simple interest** interest calculated on the principal, or the initial amount of money invested or borrowed

Think About It

In the 2000 baseball season, 3,055,000 fans attended the New York Yankees' home games. In 2004, the home attendance for Yankees games was 3,775,000. What was the percent of change in home attendance between 2000 and 2004?

Samantha deposits $200.00 in a bank account. The interest rate is 6% per year. How much simple interest will the account earn in three years?

Here's How

Percent of Change

Step 1 Subtract to determine the amount of change.

$$\text{amount of change} = \text{attendance in 2004} - \text{attendance in 2000}$$
$$= 3,775,000 - 3,055,000$$

What is the amount of change? _____

Step 2 Divide to determine the percent of change.

$$P = \frac{\text{amount of change}}{\text{original amount}} = \frac{720,000}{3,055,000}$$

What is the percent of change rounded to the nearest whole percent? _____

Is the change of percent an increase or a decrease? Explain.

_____

_____

Simple Interest

Step 1 Use the simple interest formula.

$I = p \cdot r \cdot t$ where I is the interest, p is the principal, r is the interest rate per year, and t is the time in years.

Step 2 Substitute. Use 0.06 for 6%.

$I = 200 \cdot 0.06 \cdot 3$

Step 3 Multiply.

$I = 36$

What is the amount the account will earn in 3 years? _____

Practice

1 The 2003 price of admission at a movie theater was $6.00. The 2004 admission price was $7.50. What was the percent increase?

   A 15%

   B 25%

   C 30%

   D 35%

2 A pair of shoes is advertised at a sale price of $40.00. The regular price of the shoes is $60.00. By what percent has the price been reduced?

   F 10%

   G 25%

   H $33\frac{1}{3}$%

   J 50%

3 Kim works at an appliance store. He receives a salary of $510.00 each month plus a 12.5% commission on all sales. In one month, his sales are $8,010.00. What are his total earnings for that month?

   A $573.75

   B $1,020.00

   C $1,511.25

   D $6,375.00

4 Mr. Garcia is lending his son Martin $2,000 for a car and charging him 3% simple interest each year. Martin will pay back the loan in 4 years. How much in interest will he pay?

   F $240.00

   G $480.00

   H $960.00

   J $1,920.00

5 A desk sells for $199.99. The sales tax on the desk is 8.25%. What is the cost of the desk including tax?

   A $208.24

   B $209.99

   C $214.77

   D $216.49

6 The Blue Heron restaurant suggests that diners pay their server a gratuity of 15%. Which amount is a reasonable tip for a bill that is $31.75?

   F $3.20

   G $4.75

   H $5.65

   J $6.35

Short-Response Question

7 A bookstore sold 7,205 mystery novels in 2003 and 6,399 mystery novels in 2004. What was the percent of change in sales of mystery novels from 2003 to 2004? Was it a percent increase or decrease? Show your work, and explain how you got your answer.

amount of change = _____

Performance indicators: **8.N.5, 8.R.10**

Think About It

The Rodriguez family went out to dinner. The bill was $39.70. They want to leave a 15% tip. How can they use estimation to compute the 15% tip?

Here's How

Step 1 Round $39.70 to $40.00.

Step 2 Find 10% of $40.00.

$$10\% \text{ of } \$40 = \frac{1}{10} \cdot \$40$$

$$= \underline{\hspace{1.5cm}}$$

Step 3 Find 5% of $40.00.

$$5\% \text{ of } \$40 = \frac{1}{2} \cdot (10\% \text{ of } \$40)$$

$$= \frac{1}{2} \cdot \$4 = \underline{\hspace{1.5cm}}$$

Step 4 Add to find the estimated tip. $4.00 + $2.00 = \underline{\hspace{1.5cm}}

Practice

1 Estimate a 15% tip for a dinner bill of $9.84.

A $1.00

B $1.25

C $1.50

D $2.00

2 Chantile's bill at a restaurant was $20.20. Which of the following shows a reasonable way to estimate a 15% tip?

F 15 • 20

G 1.5 • 20

H 1.5 • 2

J 0.15 • 2

3 What is a reasonable estimate for a 20% tip if the bill for a meal is $79.95?

A $16.00

B $15.50

C $14.00

D $12.00

4 Estimate a 15% tip for a dinner bill of $38.02.

F $4.00

G $5.50

H $6.00

J $6.50

5 A restaurant automatically adds a 10% tip to the bill for delivered meals. Estimate the tip if the bill is $72.40.

A $5.00

B $7.20

C $10.30

D $14.40

6 Which of the following is a reasonable way to estimate a 20% tip for a dinner bill of $27.55?

F $\frac{1}{20} \cdot 28$

G $\frac{1}{10} \cdot 28$

H $\frac{2}{10} \cdot 28$

J $2 \cdot 28$

7 Gary wants to buy a New York Giants football jersey that costs $64.95. His parents will pay 25% of the cost. Estimate how much his parents will contribute.

A $13.00

B $14.50

C $16.00

D $18.50

8 If Deborah signs up for a full year of violin lessons, she will pay 20% less than the usual price of $558.50. Estimate the amount of money that Deborah will save.

F $105.00

G $108.00

H $110.00

J $112.00

9 A news report predicts that next year the price of gasoline will rise 15% above the current price. If the current price of gasoline is $2.48, which would be the best estimate of next year's price?

A $2.70

B $2.75

C $2.85

D $2.90

10 In its first year, Astrowheels, Inc. sold 51,021 minibikes. This year the company hopes to increase sales by 25%. Estimate the number of minibikes the company will have to sell to meet its goal.

F 60,000

G 63,000

H 65,000

J 70,000

Short-Response Question

11 This year's school bake sale is expected to earn about 35% more than last year's total of $234.75. What would be the best estimate for the amount earned at this year's sale?

_____

_____

_____

_____

Think About It

For his birthday, Hideki received a $75.00 gift certificate to the computer store. He picked out a computer game for $49.99, a package of disks for $10.99, a mouse pad for $2.42, and an Internet guide for $17.11. Can he pay for all of these items with his gift certificate?

Here's How

Estimate the prices of the items by rounding the prices to a convenient place value.

1. Look at the amounts. Is it more helpful to round them to whole dollars or to tenths of a dollar?
   _____

2. Which amounts should you round up? _____

3. Which amounts should you round down? _____

4. What are the values of the rounded numbers? _____

5. What is the sum of the rounded numbers? _____

Compare the estimated sum with the original amount to see how reasonable the estimate is.

6. Is the estimated sum greater than or less than the amount of the gift certificate?
   _____

7. Based on the estimate, can Hideki pay for all the items with his gift certificate? _____

8. Find the exact sum. _____
   Is the estimate reasonably close to the actual sum of the prices? _____

Practice

1 What is the best estimate of the sum of 29.81 + 31.99, when they are each rounded to the nearest whole number?

  A 60   **C** 61.8

  B 61   **D** 62

2 What is the best estimate of the difference of 12.5 − 6.2, when they are each rounded to the nearest whole number?

  F 7   **H** 6.3

  G 6.5   **J** 6

3 What is the best estimate of the difference of 1,444 − 288, when they are each rounded to the nearest hundred?

  A 1,200   **C** 1,100

  B 1,160   **D** 700

4 What is the best estimate of the sum of 72.14% + 19.33%, when they are each rounded to the nearest whole percent?

  F 90%   **H** 92%

  G 91%   **J** 93%

5 What is the best estimate of the quotient of 16.9 ÷ 3.9, when they are each rounded to the nearest whole number?

A 4   **C** 4.33

B 4.25   **D** 5

6 What is the best estimate of the difference of 22.975% − 6.003%, when they are each rounded to the nearest tenth of a percent?

F 17%   **H** 16.9%

G 16.972%   **J** 16%

7 What is the best estimate of the product of 7 • 297.554, when the second factor is rounded to the nearest hundred?

A 1,400   **C** 2,100

B 2,000   **D** 2,200

8 What is the best estimate of the sum of 313 + 258, when they are each rounded to the nearest ten?

F 600   **H** 570

G 571   **J** 560

Extended-Response Question

9 **Part A** Karen is shopping for summer clothes. She has $200 in her account. She makes a list to be sure she does not exceed that amount. Estimate the prices of the items on her list. Write your estimates in the chart. Find the total and add 6% as sales tax for purchases above $120. Show the total that Karen will need to buy the items on her list.

       Part B Use a calculator to get the exact answers and write them in the chart. Were the estimates reasonable? _____ Explain why or why not.

_____

_____

Item	Listed Price	Estimated Price	Exact Price
Cotton sweater	$29 − $\frac{1}{3}$ off		
Cotton twill pants	$54		
T-shirts: 1 yellow 1 white 1 black	3 for $9.99		
Sneakers, white	$39.99 − 25% off		
Jeans	$39 − $\frac{1}{2}$ off		
Shorts	$26.99 − $\frac{1}{3}$ off		
Bathing suit	$19.99 − $\frac{1}{4}$ off		
Total $ for purchases			
Tax 6% on purchases above $120			
Total			

Lesson 7 · Focus on Problem Solving: Develop More Efficient Methods

Performance indicator: **8.PS.1, 8.N.4**

Think About It

The Rosalias are having dinner at Turtle Crossing. The dinner costs $149.22. There is a 5% tax, and they want to leave a 15% tip. How can you figure out the tip, tax, and the total cost of the dinner?

Here's How

Use a calculator to determine the tax.

1. Is the tax added to or subtracted from the dinner cost? _____

2. To find the cost of the dinner, including tax, what percent should you use? _____

3. Which two operations can you use to compute the answer? _____

_____

4. Input the amounts on the calculator. (Steps may differ for your calculator.)

Press		1	4	9	.	2	2
Press							×
Press						5	%
Display			7	.	4	6	1
Press							+
Press		1	4	9	.	2	2
Press							=
Display	1	5	6	.	6	8	1
Round to 2 decimals		1	5	6	.	6	8

5. How can you quickly check if this amount is correct? _____

6. The bill for dinner with tax is _____.

Use mental math to quickly determine the total cost.

1. You can add 5% to 15% to calculate the total tax plus tip. 5% + 15% = _____

2. It is not necessary to find an exact amount when you tip. Round the cost of the dinner up to $150.

3. Multiplying by 20% is the same as dividing by _____.

4. To find 20% of the dinner cost, divide _____ by 50. How much is 20%? _____

5. What is the total of the dinner cost, including tax and tip? _____

Using numbers that divide easily is an efficient method of estimating.

Copying is illegal. Measuring Up® to the New York State Learning Standards

🔑 Practice

1 The Broadway play *Cats* closed on September 10, 2000, after a record-breaking 7,485 performances. Select the *best* choice for estimating the year in which the play opened if there were 7 shows each week?

A multiply by 350

B divide by 350

C multiply by 7 and then by 50

D divide by 7 and then by 50

2 In the 1959–1960 Broadway season, 7.9 million people attended Broadway plays. The performances grossed $46 million. In the 1999–2000 season, 11.4 million people attended shows and the performances grossed $603 million. Select the best choice for finding out how much more Broadway tickets cost in 1999–2000.

F calculator: division and subtraction

G calculator: addition and multiplication

H calculator: addition and division

J mental math: subtraction and multiplication

3 If you buy a sweatshirt, you first get $\frac{1}{4}$ off the original price of $48 and then an additional 10% off the marked-down price. How can you find the total discount?

A $58\frac{3}{4}$ • 0.9 using paper and pencil

B $48 • 0.65 using paper and pencil

C ($48 • 0.75) • 0.10 using a calculator

D $48 − (48 • 0.75 • 0.90) using a calculator

Short-Response Question

4 Your salary is $217.50 for working 5 hours on Monday and on Tuesday, 6 hours on Wednesday and Thursday, and 8 hours on Friday. How can you use a calculator to find your hourly wage?

Press						5
Press						+
Press						
Press						+
Display						
Press						6
Press						+
Display						
Press						6
Press						+
Display						
Press						
Press						=
Display						
Press						Clear
Press	2	1	7	.	5	0
Press						÷
Press						
Press						=
Display			7	.		

READY REFERENCE

Properties of Equality

additive property equal quantities can be added to each side of an equation without affecting the equation's truth value; *example:* $8 = 8$ and $8 + 6 = 8 + 6$ are both true equations

subtraction property equal quantities can be subtracted from each side of an equation without affecting the equation's truth value; *example:* $8 = 8$ and $8 - 6 = 8 - 6$ are both true equations

multiplication property each side of an equation can be multiplied by the same quantity without affecting the equation's truth value; *example:* $8 = 8$ and $8 \times 6 = 8 \times 6$ are both true equations

division property each side of an equation can be divided by the same quantity without affecting the equation's truth value; *example:* $8 = 8$ and $\frac{8}{6} = \frac{8}{6}$ are both true equations

 Think About It

Sometimes you can solve an equation using number sense or by guessing and checking. But there are other methods you can use that are quicker and more convenient.

How do you find the value of x that will make this equation true?

$$\frac{x + 3}{2} = 30$$

 Here's How

Step 1 Use multiplication to eliminate the denominator on the left side of the equation.

$$\frac{x + 3}{2} \cdot 2$$

Step 2 Since you multiplied one side of the equation by 2, you must also multiply the other side of the equation by 2.

$$\frac{x + 3}{2} \cdot 2 = 30 \cdot 2$$

$$x + 3 = \underline{\qquad}$$

Step 3 Use the subtraction property of equality to isolate x.

$$x + 3 - 3 = 60 - 3$$

$$x = \underline{\qquad}$$

Practice

1 In the equation $y - 248 = 321$, what is the first thing you must do?

 A Subtract 248 from both sides of the equation.

 B Add 248 to both sides of the equation.

 C Multiply both sides of the equation by 248.

 D Divide both sides of the equation by 248.

2 Solve $y - 248 = 321$.

 F 1.29

 G 73

 H 569

 J 79,608

3 Amanda notices that 7 more than the product of 5 and her basketball number is equal to 122. Use the properties of equality to find Amanda's number.

 A 115

 B 75

 C 31

 D 23

4 Samuel and Amy are playing a number game. Samuel tells Amy that his magic number is greater than 12 but less than 16. Samuel then chooses a second magic number greater than his first. Using the numerical relationships, the sum of Samuel's two magic numbers must be which of the following?

 F less than 12

 G less than 20

 H less than 26, but greater than 20

 J greater than 26

5 Sixty decreased by the product of 8 and a number is equal to 4. Using the properties of equality, which is the correct value of the number?

 A −4

 B 6

 C 7

 D 9

6 Anne is solving the equation $3x - 18 = 24$. Using the properties of equality, which number should Anne conclude is the value of x?

 F 14

 G 6

 H −2

 J −6

Short-Response Question

7 John is trying to solve the puzzle shown below at the Finley Mathematics Fair. Each letter represents a different number greater than 0. Which number should John conclude is the value of *D*?

_____

_____

_____

$$(B) \times (A) = (B)$$
$$(A) + (A) = (B)$$
$$(A) + (B) = (D)$$

Think About It

The Tri-City Baseball Association needs to raise $500 to upgrade a baseball field. The Association had a chili cook-off and raised $238.82. Sales of refreshments at games brought in $121.94. A raffle raised $87.33. The treasurer of the Association estimates that about $50.00 more is needed to pay for the field. Is this estimate reasonable?

Here's How

Step 1 Estimate.

1. To get a quick estimate of the totals, round each number to the nearest ten dollars. Then add the rounded amounts.

$238.82 rounds to _____
$121.94 rounds to _____
$87.93 rounds to + _____
_____
450.00

2. Which is larger, the estimated sum of the money raised or the amount needed for the new baseball field? _____

Step 2 Subtract.

3. Subtract to find how much more is needed to pay for the field.

$500.00 − 450.00 = _____

Step 3 Check your work using another method.

4. Use a calculator to solve the problem using the actual amounts. What is the actual total of the money raised?

_____

5. What is the actual amount needed to pay for the field?

_____

Step 4 Compare solutions.

6. Compare the actual answer with the estimated answer. Is the treasurer's estimate reasonable?

_____

 **Practice**

Look at the estimate of the answer for each expression. Do your own estimate to decide if the estimate in the chart is reasonable or not reasonable. Then use paper and pencil or a calculator to find the actual answer.

Expression	Estimate	Reasonable or Not Reasonable?	Actual Answer
1. $6.299 + 3.8 =$	10		
2. $30.922 - 5.55 =$	24		
3. $3\frac{1}{3} + 2\frac{1}{8} =$	6		
4. $2{,}499 - 9.7 =$	2,490		
5. $4\frac{7}{8} - 1\frac{1}{16} =$	2		
6. $33.62\% + 30.2\% =$	53%		
7. $8{,}001 \times 29.6 =$	240,000		
8. $15\frac{5}{12} \div 3\frac{1}{10} =$	5		
9. $3.21 \div .422 =$	8		
10. $198{,}000 \times 4.922 =$	800,000		
11. $.23 \times .8732 =$	0.2		
12. $70.702 \div 6.661 =$	10		

1 For the first game of a weekend series with the Atlanta Braves, the New York Mets drew a crowd of 37,822. Attendance for the second game of the series was 42,285. The Mets' general manager hopes to have attendance of 120,000 for the three games. Which is the best estimate of what the attendance for the last game will have to be to reach the goal?

A 35,000   **C** 40,000

B 38,000   **D** 45,000

2 On its first weekend of release, a new movie makes $14,845,237. The next weekend, the same movie makes 20% less. Which is the best estimate for the movie's earnings on the second weekend?

F $10,000,000   **H** $13,000,000

G $12,000,000   **J** $14,000,000

Short-Response Question

3 Walter is buying new clothes at a store offering a 15% discount on all purchases. He wants to buy three pairs of pants at $14.77 each, two shirts at $16.12 each, and a pair of shoes at $32.98. Walter estimates that his total bill will be around $85.00. Do you agree or disagree? Explain your answer.

> **READY REFERENCE**
>
> **irrational number**   a number that cannot be written as a simple fraction; it is an infinite and non-repeating decimal
>
> π pi, the ratio of the circumference of a circle to its diameter

Think About It

The square root of 3 is an irrational number. Latoya wants to estimate the value of this square root. How should she go about finding her answer?

Here's How

Estimate the value of irrational numbers.

Step 1 Write the irrational number that you want to estimate.

square root of 3, or $\sqrt{3}$

Step 2 Think of a number that is a perfect square and is close to but smaller than 3. Ask yourself, is 2 a perfect square? If not, go to the next smaller number until you find one that is a perfect square. Find its square root.

square root of 1, or $\sqrt{1} = 1$

Step 3 Think of a number that is a perfect square and is close to but larger than 3. Ask yourself, is 4 a perfect square? Yes, 4 is a perfect square. Then find its square root.

square root of 4, or $\sqrt{4} = 2$

Step 4 Use the values you found to record your estimate as a range.

$\sqrt{3}$ is between 1 and ____.

Estimate the value of an irrational number to the closest hundredth.

The value of π (pi) is an irrational number, a non-repeating, non-terminating decimal. To the first 10 decimal places, the value of π is 3.1415926535.

Step 1 To estimate the value of an irrational number to the nearest hundredth, find the digit that is in the hundredths place.

digit in the hundredths place ____

Step 2 Look at the digit to its right. If that number is less than 5, record the digit in the hundredths place as it is written. If the number is 5 or greater, round the digit in the hundredths place up by 1.

Rounded to the nearest hundredth,

3.1415926535 ≈ _____

Practice

1 Estimate the value of π (3.1415926535) to the nearest thousandth.

A 3.14   C 3.142

B 3.141   D 3.1416

2 Between what two consecutive whole numbers does the square root of 35 fall?

F 4 and 5   H 6 and 7

G 5 and 6   J 7 and 8

3 Which of the following is the best estimate of the value of the square root of 5?

A between 1 and 3

B between 2 and 3

C between 2 and 4

D between 3 and 4

4 The decimal equivalent of $\frac{1}{3}$ is 0.3333. Estimate the value of this number to the nearest tenth.

F 0.3

G 0.4

H 0.33

J 0.34

5 Find the two consecutive numbers that the square root of 71 falls between.

A between 5 and 6

B between 6 and 7

C between 7 and 8

D between 8 and 9

6 The decimal equivalent of the fraction $\frac{2}{3}$ is 0.6666. Estimate the value of this number to the nearest hundredth.

F 0.6

G 0.7

H 0.66

J 0.67

7 Which of the following is the best estimate of the value of the square root of 28?

A between 6 and 7

B between 5 and 6

C between 4 and 5

D between 3 and 4

8 Estimate the value of the square root of 12.

F between 2 and 3

G between 3 and 4

H between 4 and 5

J between 5 and 6

Short-Response Question

9 Which number is greater, 12 or the square root of 149? Explain how you arrived at your answer.

_____

_____

_____

Performance indicator: **8.R.1, 8.R.8**

Think About It

On a number line, negative integers are to the left of zero and positive integers are to the right of zero. You can locate integers on a number line and use it to add and multiply integers.

Here's How

Locate integers on a number line.

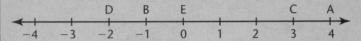

1. The letter A is located at _____ on the number line.

2. The letter B is located at _____ on the number line.

3. The opposite of −2 has the letter _____ above it.

Use a number line to find the sum of −5 + (−3).

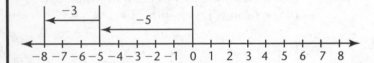

Step 1 Start at zero.

Step 2 Move 5 units to the left to −5.

Step 3 To add −3 to −5, move 3 units to the left of −5. So, −5 + (−3) = _____.

Use a number line to find the sum of −3 + 4.

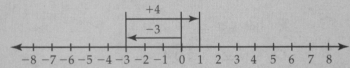

Step 1 Start at zero.

Step 2 Move 3 units to the left to −3.

Step 3 To add 4 to −3, move 4 units to the right of −3. So, (−3) + 4 = ___.

Use a number line to find the product of 3 • (−2).

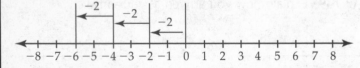

Step 1 Start at zero.

Step 2 Move 2 units to the left. This represents −2.

Step 3 Repeat this 2 more times to represent $3 \times (-2)$. So, $3 \times (-2)$ = _____.

Practice

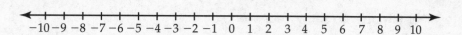

$-10\ -9\ -8\ -7\ -6\ -5\ -4\ -3\ -2\ -1\ \ 0\ \ 1\ \ 2\ \ 3\ \ 4\ \ 5\ \ 6\ \ 7\ \ 8\ \ 9\ \ 10$

1 Use the number line to find the sum of $-3 + 5$.

A -3

B -2

C $+2$

D $+5$

2 Use the number line to find $-1 \cdot 4$.

F -5

G -4

H $+3$

J $+4$

3 Use the number line to find $-3 + 8$.

A -5

B -2

C $+5$

D $+11$

4 Use the number line to find the value of $-4 \cdot 2$.

F -8

G -6

H -2

J $+4$

5 Use the number line to find $-4 + (-5)$.

A -9

B -1

C $+1$

D $+9$

6 Use the number line to find $-5 \cdot 2$.

F $+3$

G -3

H -7

J -10

Short-Response Questions

7 What addition problem does this model show?

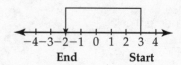

$-4\ -3\ -2\ -1\ \ 0\ \ 1\ \ 2\ \ 3\ \ 4$
End   **Start**

_____

8 What addition problem does this model show?

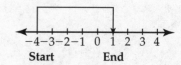

$-4\ -3\ -2\ -1\ \ 0\ \ 1\ \ 2\ \ 3\ \ 4$
Start   **End**

_____

Directions

Use a separate sheet of paper to show your work.

1 What is the exponent x in the expression $6^9 \cdot 6^3 = 6^x$?

A 27

B 12

C 6

D 3

2 What is the exponent x in the expression $7^3 \div 7^5 = 7^x$?

F -2

G 2

H 8

J 15

3 Evaluate 7^3.

A 2.67

B 10

C 21

D 343

4 Evaluate $(-4^2 + 4) \div 2^2$.

F -2

G 2

H -3

J 10

5 How do you write 39.792 as a percent?

A 39.792%

B 397.92%

C 3,979.2%

D 39,792%

6 How do you write 0.0123 as a percent?

F 123%

G 12.3%

H 1.23%

J 0.123%

7 What is 120% of 65?

A 780

B 78

C 7.8

D 0.78

8 What is 0.01% of 6,666?

F 0.6666

G 6.666

H 6.66

J 66.66

9 Shania works at a clothing store in the mall and receives a 10% discount on all her purchases there. Her favorite pair of jeans costs $59.99, but they are on sale for 25% off. How much will Shania pay for the jeans after taking her discount off the sales price? Round your answer to the nearest cent.

A $53.99

B $40.49

C $38.99

D $36.49

Measuring Up® to the New York State Learning Standards

10 Mrs. Graydeer buys a bond for $2,500.00. The bond pays 3% interest per year. How much money will Mrs. Graydeer receive if she cashes in the bond after one year?

F $75.00

G $250.00

H $2,575.00

J $3,250.00

11 Estimate a 20% tip for a dinner bill of $63.99.

A $6.40

B $9.60

C $12.80

D $13.00

12 CDs are sold at a local store for $13.00. However, customers who buy 3 CDs get a 10% discount. How much will Jason save if he buys 3 CDs by his favorite singer?

F $3.60

G $3.90

H $4.20

J $4.50

13 Which is the *best* estimate of the quotient of 95.7 ÷ 12.1, when they are each rounded to the nearest whole number?

A 7

B 8

C 9

D 10

14 Which is the *best* estimate of the difference of 43.5% − 22.7%, when they are each rounded to the nearest percent?

F 23%

G 21.8%

H 21%

J 19%

15 Which is the *best* estimate of the product of 90 • 284.5231, when the factor with the decimal is rounded to the nearest hundred?

A 2,610

B 2,700

C 26,100

D 27,000

16 Which is an estimate of the sum of 967 + 322, when they are each rounded to the nearest ten?

F 1,290

G 1,289

H 1,200

J 1,000

17   **Part A**   Francine is earning $7.00 per hour. She gets a 20% raise in pay.

How much more per hour will she earn?

_____

What will Francine's new hourly rate be?

_____

If Francine worked 30 hours at her old rate, how much did she earn?

_____

Part B   Next week, Francine is scheduled to work 32 hours at her new hourly rate. How much should she expect to earn?

_____

Part C   Suppose Francine gets another 15% raise next year. How much can she then expect to earn for working 32 hours in one week?

_____

_____

_____

18   **Part A**   The Booster Club is running a concession stand at the volleyball tournament. The club's goal is to make a total profit of $1,500. Evan made a table to show how much profit the club made during the first 4 hours the concession stand was open. If the club continues to make about the same profit each hour as they did in hours 3 and 4, estimate how many more hours it will take until the club reaches its goal.

Part B   Complete the chart.

Hour	Profit Made
1	$245
2	$237
3	$269
4	$270

_____

_____

_____

_____

READY REFERENCE

inequality a comparison of two expressions that uses one of the symbols $<$, $>$, $\leq$, $\geq$, or $\neq$

$<$ is less than $\qquad$ $\leq$ is less than or equal to $\qquad$ $\neq$ is not equal to

$>$ is greater than $\qquad$ $\geq$ is greater than or equal to

 Think About It

Mathematical ideas can be expressed verbally using words. They can also be expressed algebraically using numbers and symbols. How can you translate a verbal expression to a mathematical expression and vice versa?

Here's How

Write a verbal expression that matches a mathematical equation.

$$9 \cdot 14 = x$$

Step 1 Suppose a group of nine students are selling badges to raise money for the choir. To reach their goal of x, what is the number of badges each student must sell? ____

Step 2 Use the information from the algebraic equation to complete this verbal expression. To reach the goal x in a fundraiser for the choir, ____ students must sell _____ each.

Create an algebraic inequality that matches a verbal concept.

Dawon takes home $7.00 for each hour he works. He wants to save money to buy a video game and still have money for a movie. The movie will cost at least $7. The game costs $39.99 plus 6% sales tax. How can this idea be expressed as an algebraic inequality?

Step 1 Choose a variable for the unknown quantity.
x = the number of hours that Dawon must work

Step 2 Write an expression that states the ideas that are known.
($7.00) $\cdot$ x = the amount that Dawon must earn for the video game, the sales tax, and the movie
$39.99 + ($39.99 \cdot 0.06$) = the total cost of the game
The cost of the movie is more than $7.

Step 3 Write an algebraic inequality that states these ideas. Since Dawon must earn more than the total cost of the game plus the minimum price of the movie, what symbol should be used to complete the inequality below?
($7.00) $\cdot$ x ____ $39.99 + ($39.99 \cdot 0.06$) + $7

 **Practice**

1 Sierra wants to buy enough dogs treats to feed Yoda 2 a day and Bear 3 a day for the 7 days she is at camp. Which inequality expresses this idea?

A $x \geq (3 + 2) \cdot 7$ **B** $x \leq (3 + 2) \cdot 7$ **C** $(3 + 2) \cdot 7 < x$ **D** $(3 + 2) \cdot 7 > x$

2 In order to win a pizza party, Mrs. Johnson's 16 students must read more than 160 books. Which inequality expresses this idea?

F $x \div 160 > 16$ **G** $160 \div 16 < x$ **H** $16 \cdot x > 160$ **J** $160 \cdot x > 16$

3 Candace wants to know how many 12-ounce packages of trail mix will fill a 22-pound tub for the refreshment stand. Which inequality expresses this idea?

A $12 \cdot 22 > x$ **B** $22 \div x > 12$ **C** $22 - x \leq 12$ **D** $x \cdot 12 \leq 22$

4 A school group is going on a field trip. Which sentence *best* describes this equation: $96 - x = 47$?

F Out of 96 students, 47 must go on the second bus after the first bus is filled.

G Out of 96 students, only 47 students can fit on the bus.

H Mr. Suarez's class of 47 students raised enough money to take 96 people on the field trip.

J In order to attend the field trip, 47 students must sell 96 tickets.

5 Which sentence *best* describes this equation: $x = 10\% \cdot \$19.98$?

A The Booster Club must increase their sales of $19.98 blankets by 10%.

B Members must buy at least 10% of the $19.98 Booster Club blankets that are for sale.

C Only 10% of the $19.98 Booster Club blankets were left after the sale.

D The price decreases by this amount when a $19.98 Booster Club blanket is on sale for 10% off.

6 Which sentence best describes this equation: $x \div 4 = 41$?

F If 41 people want books, 4 will be left over after a bag of books is shared.

G If 4 people take books, then there must be 41 books in the bag.

H If a bag of books is divided into sets of 4 books, then 41 people will receive 4 books each.

J If the books in a bag cost $4.00 each, then the entire bag will sell for $42.00.

Short-Response Questions

7 Write an inequality that shows the speed a car must achieve in order to travel over 300 miles in 5 hours.

_____

8 Write a sentence that describes this equation: $\$77.74 \div \$2.99 = x$.

_____

_____

Lesson 13 | Describe a Situation Involving Relationships that Match a Given Graph

Performance indicators: **8.A.3, 8CM.10**

READY REFERENCE

number line a diagram that shows numbers in order on a line

coordinate plane a plane divided into four quadrants defined by the horizontal *x*-axis and the vertical *y*-axis

---

 Think About It

Relationships can be presented on a number line and on a graph. How can you describe the situations that match a number line and a graph?

 Here's How

Write an inequality that represents the points shown on the number line.

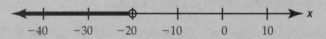

-40   -30   -20   -10   0   10   →x

Step 1 Let *x* equal all the numbers that will make the inequality true.

Step 2 The open circle at −20 shows that the numbers in the set are less than but *not* equal to −20. Use < to show that *x* is less than −20.

Step 3 Write the inequality that matches the concept shown on the number line. _____

Write an equality that represents the points that form a line on a graph.

x	?	y
0	$40 + \underline{\quad} \cdot 0$	40
2	$40 + \underline{\quad} \cdot 2$	50
4	$40 + \underline{\quad} \cdot 4$	60
6	$40 + \underline{\quad} \cdot 6$	70
8	$40 + \underline{\quad} \cdot 8$	80

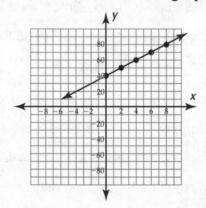

The graph shows the cost of a one-month trial membership at a health club. The *x*-values represent the number of visits to the club. The *y*-values represent _____.

Step 1 Complete the table.

Step 2 Describe the situation using words and numbers. The cost equals a basic fee, _____, plus a cost per visit _____, multiplied by _____.

Step 3 Write an equation to match the graph.
$y = 40 + \underline{\quad\quad}$

30 Mathematics • Level H   Copying is illegal.   Measuring Up® to the New York State Learning Standards

Practice

For questions 1–4, complete the table of ordered pairs for the equation given. Then use the values in your table to determine which of the graphs shown below represents this equation.

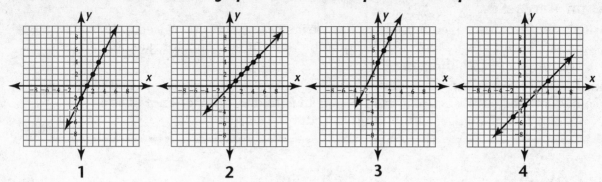

1

2

3

4

1 $y = x$

A Graph 1

B Graph 2

C Graph 3

D Graph 4

x	y
−2	
−1	
0	
1	
2	

2 $y = x - 3$

F Graph 1

G Graph 2

H Graph 3

J Graph 4

x	y
−2	
−1	
0	
1	
2	

3 $y = 2x - 2$

A Graph 1

B Graph 2

C Graph 3

D Graph 4

x	y
−2	
−1	
0	
1	
2	

4 $y = 2x + 4$

F Graph 1

G Graph 2

H Graph 3

J Graph 4

x	y
−2	
−1	
0	
1	
2	

Extended-Response Question

5 **Part A** Examine the graph. Then, complete the table below by finding the value of *y* for each value of *x*.

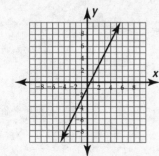

x	?	y
1	2 − 1	
2	4 − 1	
3	6 − 1	
4	8 − 1	

Part B Describe a situation that matches the graph.

_____

_____

READY REFERENCE

linear relationship an equation that has variables on each side raised only to the first power, such as $y = 3x - 8$; the equation describes a constant rate of change; its graph is a straight line

nonlinear relationship an equation that has variables on each side raised to a power other than 1, such as $y = 4x^2 + 10$; an equation that does not have a constant rate of change; a graph that is a curve

---

 Think About It

The graph of a linear relationship is a straight line. The graph of a nonlinear relationship is generally not straight, but is curved instead.

 Here's How

Determine if the relationship is linear or nonlinear.

$y = \frac{2}{3}x + 1$

Step 1 Variable x is raised to the _____ power.

Step 2 Variable y is raised to the _____ power.

Step 3 Since the variables on each side are raised to the _____ power, the equation represents a _____ relationship.

Create a graph of the relationship.

Step 1 Develop a table of ordered pairs for the equation. Then use the values in your table to graph the equation.

Step 2 Plot the ordered pairs on the coordinate plane.

Step 3 Connect the points to form the graph of the linear relationship.

x	$y = \frac{2}{3}x + 1$	y
0	$\frac{2}{3}(0) + 1$	___
3	$\frac{2}{3}(3) + 1$	___
6	$\frac{2}{3}(6) + 1$	___
9	$\frac{2}{3}(9) + 1$	___

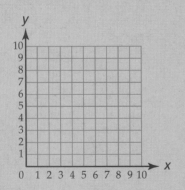

 **Practice**

1 Which relationship is linear?

A $y = x^2 \div 3$ **C** $x + y = 8$

B $x^2 + y^2 = 1$ **D** $y = x^2 + 3x - 2$

2 Which relationship is nonlinear?

F $y = -2x + 9$ **H** $x + y = 8$

G $y = 3x + (x \div 4)$ **J** $y = -6x^3 + 1$

For questions 3–4, complete the table and graph the ordered pairs in the table. Then, identify the equation that corresponds to the graph.

3

x	?	y
0	$(0 + 1)2$	
1	$(1 + 1)2$	
2	$(2 + 1)2$	

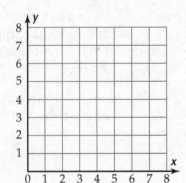

A $y = x^2 + 1$ **C** $y = 2x^2 + 1$

B $y = 2(x + 1)$ **D** $y = (x^3 + 1)2$

4

x	?	y
-2	$4 - 1$	
-1	$1 - 1$	
0	$0 - 1$	
1	$1 - 1$	
2	$4 - 1$	

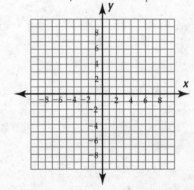

F $y = x + 2x - 1$ **H** $y = x^2 - 1$

G $y = (3x \div x) - 1$ **J** $y = (x \cdot 2) - 1$

Extended-Response Question

5 The equation $y = x + 4$ expresses the number of DVDs, y, Brent receives from his DVD club each month, where x is the number of months he has been a member.

Part A
Complete the table to show how many DVDs Brent receives each month

x	$y = x + 4$	y
1	$1 + 4$	
2	$2 + 4$	
3	$3 + 4$	
4	$4 + 4$	

Part B
Graph the equation on the coordinate plane.

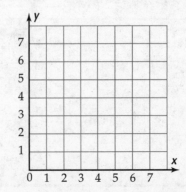

Performance indicators: **8.A.5, 8.R.1**

READY REFERENCE

monomial a number, a variable, or a product of numbers and variables
polynomial an algebraic expression containing one or more monomials

---

 Think About It

How can you use models to perform a mathematical operation with two polynomials, such as $(3x^2 + x - 4) + (2x^2 + 3x + 6)$ or $(3x - 2) \cdot (2x + 3)$?

Here's How

Make a model showing the addition of two polynomials.

A polynomial is an expression that contains one or more monomials, such as x^2, $7x$, or 16. To make a model of a polynomial, you must have a different model for each kind of monomial in it.

Step 1 Make a model of the two polynomials.

Step 2 Add the polynomials by combining like terms and removing zero pairs. A zero pair is a box and its opposite, such as 1 and −1.

Step 3 Write the polynomial for the boxes that remain.

$(3x^2 + x - 4) + (2x^2 + 3x + 6) =$

_____ + _____ + _____

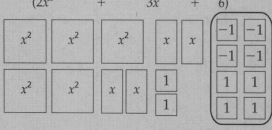

Make a model showing the multiplication of two polynomials.

Step 1 Make a model showing multiplication of the two polynomials. Inside the square, multiply each model in the left column by a model in the bottom row.

Step 2 Combine the like terms, eliminate any zero pairs, and write the polynomial for the boxes that remain.

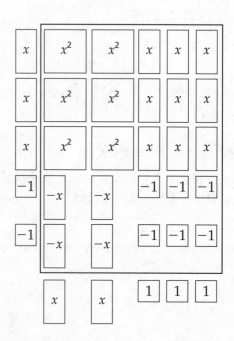

Copying is illegal.
Measuring Up® to the New York State Learning Standards

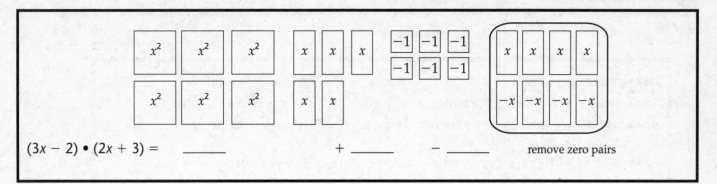

$(3x - 2) \cdot (2x + 3) =$ _____   +_____   −_____   remove zero pairs

Practice

1 Which is the correct sum of the polynomials in this model?

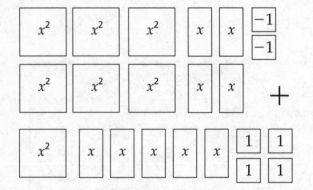

A $5x^2 - x + 6$ **C** $6x^2 + 9x + 4$

B $7x^2 + 9x + 2$ **D** $7x^2 + 9x - 2$

2 Look at the model. Which is the correct product of these two polynomials?

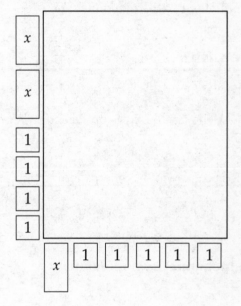

F $3x + 9$ **H** $2x^2 + 9x + 20$

G $2x^2 + 9x - 20$ **J** $2x^2 + 20$

Short-Response Question

3 In the space at right, draw a model that represents the following expression:

$(3x^2 + 5x + 4) + (4x^2 + 2x - 5)$

The sum is

_____ .

Performance indicators: **8.A.6, 8.N.1**

READY REFERENCE

monomial a number, a variable, or a product of numbers and variables

product of powers for any real number a and positive integers m
and n: $a^m \cdot a^n = a^{m+n}$

quotient of powers for any nonzero number a and integers m
and n: $\frac{a^m}{a^n} = a^{m-n}$

 Think About It

What is the product of the monomials $5x^3$ and $-3x^2$?

What is the quotient of the monomials $\frac{f^9}{f^6}$

 Here's How

Multiply two monomials. $(5x^3)(-3x^2)$

Step 1   Use the commutative and associative properties to group coefficients and variables.

$(5x^3)(-3x^2) = [(5 \cdot (-3))](x^3 \cdot x^2)$

Step 2   Use the law of exponents for multiplication.

$= (-15)(x^{3+2})$

$= \underline{\hspace{2cm}}$

Divide a monomial by a monomial.

$\frac{f^9}{f^6}$

Step 1   Use the law of exponents for division.

$\frac{f^9}{f^6} = f^{9-6}$

$= \underline{\hspace{1.5cm}}$

 Practice

Find each product or quotient in exponential form.

 1 $b \cdot b^4$

A $2b^5$ **C** b^3

B b^5 **D** b^2

2 $a^4 \cdot a^7$

F a^{-3} **H** a^{11}

G a^3 **J** a^{28}

3 $9^6 \cdot 9^2$

A 9^4 **C** 9^{12}

B 9^8 **D** 9^{24}

4 $3^{-3} \cdot 3^3$

F 3^0 **H** 3^6

G 3^1 **J** 3^9

5 $x^5 \cdot x^{-4} \cdot x^7$

A x^{-2} **C** x^7

B x^2 **D** x^8

6 $(7x^4)(2x^3)$

F $5x$ **H** $14x^7$

G $14x^{-1}$ **J** $14x^{12}$

7 $(-3y^4)(-y^8)$

A $-11y^3$ **C** $24y^3$

B $5y^5$ **D** $3y^{12}$

8 $(-4b^{11})(8b^{-2})$

F $-32b^9$ **H** $4b^9$

G $-32b^{22}$ **J** $32b^{13}$

9 $(a^7)(3a^3)$

A a^4 **C** $3a^{10}$

B $3a^4$ **D** $3a^{21}$

10 $(25x^{-8})(-4x^3)$

F $21x^{-5}$ **H** $-100x^{11}$

G $-100x^{-5}$ **J** $100x^{-5}$

11 $\dfrac{7^9}{7^4}$

A 7^3 **C** 7^{13}

B 7^5 **D** 7^{36}

12 $\dfrac{d^7}{d^5}$

F d^2 **H** d^{12}

G d^4 **J** d^{17}

13 $\dfrac{p^2}{p^5}$

A p^{-7} **C** p^3

B p^{-3} **D** p^7

14 $\dfrac{(-7)^3}{(-7)^2}$

F $(-7)^1$ **H** 7^{-1}

G $(-7)^6$ **J** 7^1

15 $\dfrac{a^4 b^5}{a^2 b^2}$

A ab^{10} **C** $a^6 b^7$

B $a^2 b^3$ **D** $a^8 b^{10}$

16 $\dfrac{x^2 y^2}{x^3 y^3}$

F $x^1 y^1$ **H** $x^{-1} y^{-1}$

G $x^2 y^2$ **J** $x^{-2} y^{-2}$

Short-Response Question

17 Explain how you would find the missing exponent in the following equation: $x^4 \cdot x^? = x^{13}$.

_____

_____

Performance indicators: **8.A.7, 8.CN.2**

 Think About It

How do you add the polynomials $(4x^2 + 5x + 6)$ and $(2x^2 - 4x + 3)$?
How do you find the difference between the polynomials $(7x^2 + 4x + 5)$ and $(5x^2 + x - 4)$?

 Here's How

Add two polynomials.

$(4x^2 + 5x + 6) + (2x^2 - 4x + 3)$

Write the polynomials vertically so that like terms are aligned. Add the like terms.

$$
\begin{array}{rrrr}
 & 4x^2 & + 5x & + 6 \\
(+) & 2x^2 & - 4x & + 3 \\
\hline
 & 6x^2 & + x & + 9 \\
\end{array}
$$

Another Option: You can add the same polynomials horizontally.

$$(4x^2 + 5x + 6) + (2x^2 - 4x + 3) = (4x^2 + 2x^2) + (5x + (-4x)) + (6 + 3)$$

$$= 6x^2 + x + 9$$

Find the difference between two polynomials.

$(7x^2 + 4x + 5) - (5x^2 + x - 4)$

Write the polynomials vertically so that like terms are aligned. Subtract the like terms.

$$
\begin{array}{rrrr}
 & 7x^2 & + 4x & + 5 \\
(-) & 5x^2 & + x & - 4 \\
\hline
 & 2x^2 & + 3x & + 9 \\
\end{array}
$$

Another Option: Subtraction is the same as addition of the opposite. You can add the opposite of the second polynomial. The opposite of a polynomial is the polynomial multiplied by -1.

$(7x^2 + 4x + 5) - (5x^2 + x - 4)$
$= (7x^2 + 4x + 5) + (-1)(5x^2 + x - 4)$ Add the opposite.
$= (7x^2 + 4x + 5) + (-5x^2 - x + 4)$
$= (7x^2 - 5x^2) + (4x - x) + (5 + 4)$ Regroup using the commutative
$= 2x^2 + 3x + 9$ property of addition.

 **Practice**

Find the sum of each pair of polynomials.

1 $(9x + 3) + (5x - 1)$

A $4x + 2$ **B** $10x + 4$ **C** $14x + 2$ **D** $45x - 3$

2 $(2x^2 + 8x + 7) + (7x^2 - 8x + 6)$

F $(9x^2 + 13)$ **G** $(9x^2 + 16x + 13)$ **H** $(-5x^2 + 1)$ **J** $(9x^2 + 3)$

3 $(8x^2 - 3x - 1) + (4x^2 - 2x + 6)$

A $12x^2 + 5x - 5$ **B** $12x^2 - 5x + 5$ **C** $4x^2 - 5x + 5$ **D** $-4x^2 + 5x - 5$

4 $(5x^2 + 7x + 12) + (-3x^2 + 6x - 10)$

F $-8x^2 + 13x - 2$ **G** $2x^2 + x - 2$ **H** $2x^2 + 13x + 2$ **J** $8x^2 + 12x - 2$

Find the additive inverse of each polynomial.

5 $7x^2 - 3x - 9$

A $7x^2 + 3x + 9$ **B** $-7x^2 - 3x - 9$ **C** $7x^2 - 3x + 9$ **D** $-7x^2 + 3x + 9$

6 $-23x^2 + 4x - 3$

F $23x^2 - 4x + 3$ **G** $-23x^2 - 4x - 3$ **H** $23x^2 + 4x - 3$ **J** $-23x^2 + 4x + 3$

Find the difference between each pair of polynomials.

7 $(6x + 8) - (2x + 5)$

A $-4x + 3$ **B** $4x + 3$ **C** $4x - 3$ **D** $-4x - 3$

8 $(2x^2 + 10x + 1) - (5x^2 + 7x + 2)$

F $7x^2 + 3x - 3$ **G** $3x^2 - 3x + 1$ **H** $-3x^2 + 3x - 1$ **J** $-3x^2 - 3x + 1$

9 $(12x^2 - 8x - 4) - (-x^2 + 4x - 9)$

A $12x^2 - 12x + 5$ **B** $11x^2 - 4x + 13$ **C** $-13x^2 + 12x - 5$ **D** $13x^2 - 12x + 5$

10 $(2x^2 - 7) - (11x^2 + 5x + 3)$

F $9x^2 + 5x + 10$ **G** $-9x^2 - 5x - 10$ **H** $13x^2 + 5x + 4$ **J** $11x^2 + 4x - 4$

Short-Response Question

11 What is the sum of a polynomial and its additive inverse? Explain your answer with an example.

_____

_____

> **READY REFERENCE**
> **binomial** a polynomial with exactly two terms; the sum of two monomials

Think About It

How can you find the product of the binomial $(2x + 4)$ and the monomial 5?
How can you find the product of the two binomials $(x + 2)$ and $(3x + 7)$?

Here's How

Find the product of a binomial and a monomial.

$$(2x + 4) \cdot 5 = (2x)5 + (4)5 \qquad \text{Use the distributive property.}$$
$$= 10x + 20$$

Find the product of two binomials.

$$(x + 2) \cdot (3x + 7)$$

Step 1 Use the distributive property to multiply by each term of the binomial.

$$= (x + 2)3x + (x + 2)7$$

Step 2 Use the distributive property again and multiply.

$$= (x)3x + (2)3x + (x)7 + (2)7$$
$$= 3x^2 + 6x + 7x + 14$$

Step 3 Add like terms.

$$= 3x^2 + 13x + 14$$

Practice

Find each product.

1 $(8x + 3) \cdot 4$

   A $8x + 12$ **B** $32x + 12$ **C** $32x + 24$ **D** $16x + 12$

2 $(2x^2 + 5) \cdot 2$

   F $(4x^2 + 10)$ **G** $(4x^2 + 10x)$ **H** $(-4x^2 - 10)$ **J** $(x^2 + 10)$

3 $(7x - 1) \cdot x$

   A $7x + 7$ **B** $6x^2 - 7x$ **C** $7x^2 + x$ **D** $7x^2 - x$

4 $(3x + 6) \cdot (-6x)$

F $-12x^2 - 12x$ **G** $18x^2 - x$ **H** $-18x^2 - 36x$ **J** $18x^2 + 36x$

5 $4x(-2x + 5)$

A $-8x^2 + 20x$ **B** $8x^2 - 2x$ **C** $-8x^2 - 20x$ **D** $-8x^2 + 20$

6 $8a(30a - 11)$

F $240a - 88$ **G** $240a^2 - 88a$ **H** $240a^2 + 88a$ **J** $-240a^2 + 88a$

7 $(3x + 5) \cdot (2x + 2)$

A $6x + 10$ **B** $6x^2 + 16x$ **C** $6x^2 + 10x + 10$ **D** $6x^2 + 16x + 10$

8 $(x + 6) \cdot (4x - 5)$

F $4x^2 + 19x - 30$ **G** $-4x^2 - 19x + 30$ **H** $5x^2 + 24x - 30$ **J** $-3x^2 - 19x + 30$

9 $(-7x - 3)(5x - 2)$

A $-35x^2 - 15x - 5$ **B** $35x^2 - 15x + 6$ **C** $-35x^2 - x + 6$ **D** $35x^2 + x - 6$

10 $(3x + 4)(-4x - 6)$

F $12x^2 + 34x + 24$ **G** $-12x^2 - 34x - 24$ **H** $12x^2 + 2x - 2$ **J** $-12x^2 - 16x - 24$

11 $(x + 2)(x - 9)$

A $x^2 - 7x - 18$ **B** $-x^2 + 7x + 18$ **C** $2x^2 - 18$ **D** $2x^2 + 2x - 18$

12 $(12x + 2)(2x + 1)$

F $-6x^2 - 8x + 2$ **G** $6x^2 + 12x + 1$ **H** $24x^2 + 4x + 2$ **J** $24x^2 + 16x + 2$

Short-Response Question

13 How can you find the product of the following binomial and monomial? Show your work and explain your answer. $(4x^3 + 7x^2)2x^2$

_____

_____

_____

_____

Performance indicators: **8.A.9, 8.CM.11**

 Think About It

How can you find the quotient of the polynomial $(3x^2 - 4)$ divided by the monomial $6x$?
How can you find the quotient of the polynomial $(8b^2 - 12b + 10)$ divided by the monomial $2b$?

Here's How

Find the quotient of a binomial and a monomial.

$(3x^2 - 4) \div 6x$

Step 1   Write as an algebraic fraction.

$$= \frac{3x^2 - 4}{6x}$$

Step 2   Divide each term by the monomial.

$$= \frac{3x^2}{6x} - \frac{4}{6x}$$

Step 3   Divide by common factors.

$$= \frac{x}{2} - \frac{2}{3x}$$

Find the quotient of a polynomial and a monomial.

$(8b^2 - 12b + 10) \div 2b$

Step 1   Write as an algebraic fraction.

$$= \frac{8b^2 - 12b + 10}{2b}$$

Step 2   Divide each term by the monomial.

$$= \frac{8b^2}{2b} - \frac{12b}{2b} + \frac{10}{2b}$$

Step 3   Divide by common factors.

$$= 4b - 6 + \frac{5}{b}$$

 Practice

Find each quotient of a polynomial and a monomial. Use the space next to the question to show your work.

1 $(x^2 + 8) \div 4$

   A $4x + 2$ **B** $x^2 + 2$ **C** $\frac{x^2}{4} + 2$ **D** $\frac{x}{4} + 4$

2 $(6x^2 - 9) \div 3x^2$

  F $2 - 3x$ **H** $2 - \frac{3}{x}$

  G $2x - \frac{3}{x^2}$ **J** $2 - \frac{3}{x^2}$

3 $\dfrac{(8x^3 - 5)}{4x^2}$

  A $2x - \frac{5}{4x}$ **C** $2x^2 - \frac{5}{4x^2}$

  B $2x - 5$ **D** $2x - \frac{5}{4x^2}$

4 $(2x^2 + 4x - 12) \div 4$

  F $\frac{x^2}{2} + 1 - \frac{3}{x}$ **H** $\frac{x^2}{2} + x - 3$

  G $\frac{x}{2} + 1 - \frac{3}{x}$ **J** $\frac{x^2}{2} + \frac{1}{x} - 3x$

5 $(9x^2 - 3x + 12) \div 6x$

  A $\frac{3x}{2} - \frac{1}{2} + \frac{2}{x}$ **C** $\frac{3x^2}{x} - 2 + \frac{2}{x}$

  B $3x^2 - \frac{1}{2} + \frac{2}{x}$ **D** $3x - \frac{x}{2} + 2$

6 $(c^4 - 9c - 27) \div 3c^3$

  F $\frac{3}{c} - 3c - \frac{9}{c}$ **H** $\frac{c}{3} - \frac{3}{c^2} - \frac{9}{c^3}$

  G $\frac{c}{3} - \frac{3}{c^2} - 9$ **J** $\frac{c}{3} - 3c - \frac{9}{c^3}$

7 $\dfrac{6x^2 + 15x + 12}{2x}$

  A $\frac{3}{x} + \frac{15}{2} + 6$ **C** $6x^2 + \frac{15}{2} + \frac{6}{x}$

  B $3x + \frac{15}{2} + \frac{6}{x}$ **D** $3x + 15x + \frac{6}{x}$

8 $\dfrac{32d^2 - 16d + 8}{8d}$

  F $4d - 8 + d$ **H** $\frac{4}{d} - 2 + \frac{1}{d}$

  G $4d - 2 + \frac{2}{d}$ **J** $4d - 2 + \frac{1}{d}$

Short-Response Question

9 What conclusion can you draw if you get a remainder of 0 when dividing a polynomial by a monomial?

Performance indicators: **8.A.10, 8.R.8**

READY REFERENCE

factor an expression that divides another expression with no remainder

common factor an expression that is a factor of two or more expressions

greatest common factor (GCF) the greatest expression that is a factor of two or more expressions

Think About It

The factors of 24 and 8 are:
24: 1, 2, 3, 4, 6, 8, 24
8: 1, 2, 4, 8

The common factors are 1, 2, 4, and 8. The greatest common factor (GCF) of 24 and 8 is 8.

These are factors and common factors of whole numbers. How can you factor algebraic expressions?

Here's How

Find the greatest common factor (GCF) of two algebraic expressions: $12a^3b$ and $40a^2b^2c$.

Step 1 What are the factors of 12? 1, 2, 3, ___, ___, ___

What are the factors of 40? 1, 2, ___, ___, ___, ___, ___, ___

What are the common factors of 12 and 40? _____

The GCF of 12 and 40 is ___.

Step 2 Identify the variables that are common to the two expressions.

The common variables are ___ and ___.

Step 3 Find the highest power of each variable that is common to both expressions.

The highest power of a that is in both expressions is ___.

The highest power of b that is in both expressionis is ___.

Step 4 Write the GCF of $12a^3b$ and $40a^3b^2c$.

Since 4 is the GCF of the numerical coefficients and the highest powers of the common variables are a^2 and b, the GCF is _____.

Practice

1 What are the factors of $45x^3y^2$?

A 1, 3, 15, 45, x, x, x, y, y,

C 1, 3, 5, 9, 15, 45, x, x, x, y

B 1, 3, 5, 9, 15, 45, x, x, y, y

D 1, 3, 5, 9, 15, 45 x, x, x, y, y

2 What are the factors of $92a^2b^4$?

F 1, 2, 4, 23, 46, a, a, b, b, b, b

H 1, 2, 4, 23, 46, 92, a, a, b, b, b, b

G 1, 2, 4, 23, 46, 92, a, a, b, b, b

J 1, 2, 46, 92, a, a, b, b, b, b

3 What are the common factors of $21m^2$ and $36m^3$?

A 1, 3, m

C 1, 7, m, m

B 1, 3, 4, 7, 9, 12, 21, 36, m, m, m

D 1, 3, m, m

4 What are the common factors of $9d^4e$ and $81d^2e^2$?

F 1, 3, 9, d, d, e

H 1, 3, 9, 27, 81, d, d, d, d, e, e

G 1, 3, 9, d, d, e, e

J 1, 3, 9, d, d, d, d, e

5 Identify the GCF of $140xy^3$ and $49x^2y$.

A $2xy$

C $7x^2y$

B $7xy^2$

D $7xy$

6 Identify the GCF of $14a^3b^2c + 7a^2$ and $28a^2c$.

F $7a^2c$

H $7a^2$

G $14a^2$

J $7(4c + 7ad)$

7 Identify the GCF of $3b^4d + 9b^3d^2$ and $45b^2cd^3 + 15b^3d^3$.

A $3b^2d$

C $3(b + 3d)$

B $3b^2d^2$

D $3(3cd + bd)$

Short-Response Question

8 Look at the factor diagram and use it to identify the GCF of $17x^2$ and $34x$.

GCF = _____

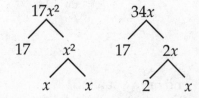

Performance indicators: **8.A.11, 8.CN.4**

> **READY REFERENCE**
> **binomial** the sum of two monomials
> **factor** an expression that divides another expression with no remainder
> **trinomial** the sum of three monomials

Think About It

An example of a trinomial is $x^2 + 12x + 32$. How is this expression factored into two binomials?

Here's How

1. To factor this trinomial, find the factors of 32.
    In the table below, write pairs of factors for 32. One has been given for you.

1	32

2. Now you must find the factors that fit in this expression. The sum of the 2 factors must equal 12.

    $x^2 + (? + ?)x + 32$

Factors of 32	Sum of Factors
1, 32	$1 + 32 = 33$
2, 16	$2 + 16 = 18$
4, 8	$4 + 8 = 12$

    Which factors can be added to equal 12? 4, ____

3. Write these factors of 32 in the binomial expressions below:
    $(x +$ ____$) (x +$ ____$)$

4. Check that these two binomials multiply to give the original trinomial:

    $(x + 4) (x + 8)$ $= (x + 4)(\underline{}) + (x + 4)(\underline{})$
    $= (x^2 + 4x) + (8x + \underline{})$
    $= x^2 + \underline{}x + 32$

    Solution: The factors of the trinomial $x^2 + 12x + 32$ are _____ and _____.

Practice

Show your work.

1 Which factors produce the product 81 and have a sum of 18?

    A 1, 81   **B** $\frac{3}{2}$, 54   **C** 3, 27   **D** 9, 9

2 Which binomials are factors of this trinomial?

$a^3 + 10a + 24$

F $(a + 4)(a + 6)$ **G** $(a + 2)(a + 12)$ **H** $(a + 3)(a + 8)$ **J** $(a + 1)(a + 24)$

3 Which numbers in the table fit the trinomial?

$b^2 + 18b + 45 = (b + \underline{\quad})(b + \underline{\quad})$

1	45
3	15
5	9

A 1, 45   **B** 3, 15   **C** 3, 9   **D** 5, 9

4 Which expression is a factor of $(b^2 + 8b + 15)$?

F $b + 15$ **G** $b + 5$ **H** $b + 8$ **J** $b + 1$

5 Factor the trinomial below.

$x^2 + 7x + 12$

Factors of 12	Sum of Factors
1, 12	13
2, 6	8
3, 4	7

A $(x + 3)(x + 4)$ **B** $(x + 6)(x + 2)$ **C** $(x + 9)(x + 2)$ **D** $(x + 12)(x + 1)$

Short-Response Question

Factors of ____	Sum of Factors

6 Factor the trinomial below by completeing the table.

$y^2 + 11y + 18$

$y^2 + 11y + 18 =$ _____

Performance indicators: **8.A.12, 8.RP.8**

READY REFERENCE

parallel lines lines in the same plane that always remain the same distance apart, as shown in Figure A

transversal a line that intersects two or more other lines

corresponding angles a pair of angles with equal measures that lie on the same side of the transversal and on the same side of each parallel line (∠1 and ∠7; ∠5 and ∠3)

vertical angles a pair of angles with equal measures that lie on opposite sides of two intersecting lines (∠1 and ∠6; ∠5 and ∠2)

alternate interior angles angles with equal measure on opposite sides of the transversal that are between the parallel lines (∠5 and ∠8; ∠6 and ∠7)

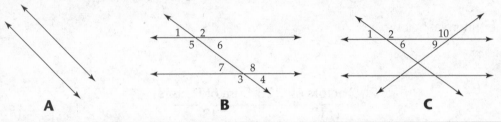

A   B   C

 Think About It

Figure A shows a pair of parallel lines. Figure B shows a pair of parallel lines that are crossed by a transversal. Figure C shows a pair of parallel lines that are crossed by a pair of lines that intersect. The transversal and intersecting lines form several pairs of angles that have the same measure.

 Here's How

Compare angles formed by two parallel lines and a transversal.

1. Look at Figure B. Together ∠1 and ∠2 form a straight angle, so their combined measure is 180°.

2. The measure of angle 2 (m∠2) is 145°. In the equation below, what does x represent? _____
    $x + 145° = 180°$

3. Solve the equation to find m∠1. $x + 145° = 180°$

    _____

    _____

4. Since ∠1 and ∠7 are corresponding angles, m∠1 = m∠7. Also, the vertical pairs of angles (∠1 and ∠6) and (∠7 and ∠4) have equal measures. Therefore, ∠1, ∠6, ∠4, and ∠7 all have the same measure. What is the measure of each of these angles?_____

5. Suppose m∠6 = $(8x)°$ and m∠7 = $(3x + 40)°$. To find the angles, set m∠6 = m∠7 and solve for x:

    $$8x = 3x + 40$$
    $$8x - 3x = 3x - 3x + 40 \qquad \text{Subtract } 3x \text{ from each side.}$$
    $$5x = 40 \qquad \text{Simplify.}$$
    $$x = 8 \qquad \text{Divide each side by 5 and simplify.}$$

    Substitute back into the original expression to find m∠6: m∠6 = $(8x)°$ = $(8 \cdot 8)°$ = _____

Compare angles formed by a pair of lines that intersect parallel lines.

Look at Figure C. You are given that m∠2 = (3x)° and m∠9 = (6x)°. You are also told that the intersecting lines are symmetrical, so m∠6 = m∠9. What are m∠2 and m∠9?

1. Angles that form a straight angle add to 180°. So,
    m∠6 = 180° − m∠2.   Substitute m∠6 = m∠9.
    m∠9 = 180° − m∠2

2. Substitute the given expressions for m∠9 and m∠2 and solve for x.
    6x = 180° − 3x
    6x + 3x = 180° − 3x + 3x   Add 3x to each side and simplify.
    9x = 180°   Divide by 9 and simplify.
    x = 20°

    Substitute back into the original expression to find m∠2 and m∠9:
    m∠2 = (3x)° = (3 • 20)° = _____
    m∠9 = (6x)° = (6 • 20)° = _____

🔑 Practice

Use the figure at the right to answer questions 1–2.

1 If the measure of ∠1 is 40°, which equation can be used to find m∠2?

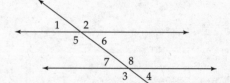

A x − 40° = 180°   **C** x = 40° + 180°

B x + 40° = 180°   **D** x = 40° − 180°

2 If the measure of ∠1 is (3x)°, what is the measure of ∠4?

F (6x)°   **G** (3x)°   **H** (180 − 6x)°   **J** (180 − 3x)°

Use the figure at the right to answer questions 3.

3 You are given that m∠2 = m∠3. If m∠1 = (4x − 30)° and m∠3 = x, what is the measure of ∠4?

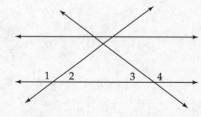

A 42°   **C** 138°

B 110°   **D** 142°

Short-Response Question

4 A transversal crosses the parallel lines below. You are given that one angle is 80°. Use algebraic equations to determine the measures of all the other angles.

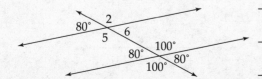

_____

_____

_____

Performance indicators: **8.A.13, 8.R.8**

READY REFERENCE

> is greater than   < is less than

≥ is greater than or equal to; is at least   ≤ is less than or equal to; is at most

---

 Think About It

With one exception, which you will see in the next lesson, you can use the same methods used for solving equations to solve inequalities. How can you solve the inequality $6x + 22 > 10$? How can you graph the solution on a number line?

 Here's How

Graph a range of values.

On the news you hear that the low temperature was above 58°F and the high was exactly 64°F. How can you graph an inequality for the range of temperatures today?

Step 1   Write two inequalities, one for the low and one for the high.

Low temperature: $t > 58$
High temperature: $t \leq$ _____

Step 2   Combine the inequalities.
$58 <$ _____ ≤ 64

Read this as "*t* was greater than 58 and less than or equal to 64."

Step 3   Graph the range of temperatures.

Put _____ circle at 58.
Put _____ circle at 64.

Draw a solid line between the circles.

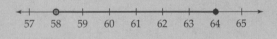

Solve a multi-step inequality.

$$6x + 22 > 10$$

Step 1   Subtract 22 from each side.

$$6x + 22 - 22 > 10 - 22$$
$$6x > -12$$

Step 2   Divide each side by 6.

$$\frac{6x}{6} > \frac{-12}{6}$$
$$x > -2$$

Graph the solution on a number line.

Step 1   Decide if $x = -2$ is part of the solution. If it is, you will put a closed circle at -2. If it is not, you will put an open circle at -2.

Is $x = -2$ part of the solution? _____

Step 2   There is an open circle at -2. The solution set includes all points greater than -2.

Step 3   Check your work by replacing x with a whole number. Using 0 often works well because the calculation is easier.

$$6(0) + 22 > 10$$
$$22 > 10 \qquad \text{true}$$

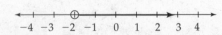

     Measuring Up® to the New York State Learning Standards

 **Practice**

Solve each inequality. Show your work in the space below the question.

1 $3x - 3 < 15$

   A $x > 6$ **B** $x < 6$ **C** $x < 15$ **D** $x > 9$

2 $2c + 14 > -10$

   F $c > -12$ **G** $c > 12$ **H** $c > -24$ **J** $c > 12$

3 $5x - 9 \geq 16$

   A $x \geq -5$ **B** $x \geq 7$ **C** $x \geq 25$ **D** $x \geq 5$

4 $27x + 6 > -3$

   F $x > -\frac{1}{3}$ **G** $x > -3$ **H** $x < -\frac{1}{3}$ **J** $9x > -3$

Solve each inequality or set of inequalities. Graph the solution on the number line provided.

5 $4c + 8 < 20$ and $c + 1 \geq 0$

Solution: _____

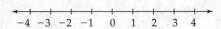

6 $18 + 2x \leq 16$

Solution: _____

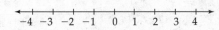

Short-Response Question

7 Write the following sentence as an inequality with numbers. Use x as the variable. The difference of five times a number and 5 is at least 10.

_____

Solve the inequality and test the truth of your solution.

_____

_____

Performance indicators: **8.A.14, 8.PS.3, 8.RP.2**

 Think About It

How can you solve the inequality $12 - 9x \leq 36 - 3x$?

 Here's How

Isolate the variables on one side of the inequality.

Step 1   Add $3x$ to each side of the inequality.

$$12 - 9x + 3x \leq 36 - 3x + 3x$$

$$12 - 6x \leq 36$$

Step 2   Subtract 12 from each side.

$$12 - 12 - 6x \leq 36 - 12$$

$$-6x \leq 24$$

Step 3   Divide each side by -6 and change the $\leq$ symbol to $\geq$.

$$\frac{-6x}{-6} \geq \frac{24}{-6}$$

$$x \geq -4$$

Graph the solution on a number line.

Step 4   Mark a closed circle at -4.

Step 5   Check your work. Replace x with a whole number, such as 0.

$$12 - 9(0) \leq 36 - 3(0)$$

$$12 \leq 36 \qquad\qquad \text{true}$$

Remember: When you multiply or divide both sides of an inequality by a negative number, the symbol of the inequality is reversed.

Use the distributive property.

Solve the inequality $3x > 4(x - 5)$

Step 1   Apply the distributive property. $3x > 4x - 20$

Step 2   Subtract $4x$ from both sides of the inequality $-x > -20$

Step 3   Multiply each side by -1 and reverse the inequality symbol. $x \underline{\hspace{1cm}} 20$

 **Practice**

Solve each inequality. Show your work.

1 $2x - 5 < 3x - 8$

   A $x > 3$ **B** $x < 3$ **C** $x < 13$ **D** $x > -13$

2 $-5a + 3 \leq 3a + 19$

   F $a \leq 8$ **G** $a \geq 2$ **H** $a \leq 16$ **J** $a \geq -2$

3 $3d - 1 > -11 - 7d$

   A $d < 11$ **B** $d > -11$ **C** $d > -1$ **D** $d < -1$

4 $-13x + 5 \geq -5x - 3$

   F $x \geq 2$ **G** $x \leq -1$ **H** $x \leq 1$ **J** $x \geq -8$

Solve the inequality. Graph the solution on the number line provided.

5 $4x - 12 \leq 6x - 18$

Solution: _____

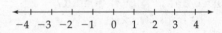

Short-Response Question

6 Write an inequality that expresses the situation in the sentence below. Use *b* as the variable. Then solve the inequality and show your work.

The number 15 decreased by six times a number is, at most, 43 minus two times the number.

Performance indicators: **8.A.15, 8.R.4, 8.R.6**

 Think About It

Mike has an after-school job that pays $6.00 an hour. He works a different number of hours every week. How would you show his daily earnings in a table? How could you represent this information in other ways?

 Here's How

Use a table of data.

How much does Mike earn each day?

Complete the table to show his earnings this week.

Look at the totals.

In _____ hours this week, Mike earned _____.

Day	Hours worked	Money earned
Monday	3	18
Tuesday	2	12
Wednesday	3	
Thursday	5	
Friday	3	
TOTALS		

Use an algebraic expression.

Step 1 Use the words in the problem to set up the expression.
$6 per hour • the number of hours worked = the amount of money Mike earns

Step 2 Use a variable in place of the known quantity.
Let h = the number of hours worked.

Step 3 Write the expression.
$6 • h or $6h$

Step 4 Use a variable for the unknown quantity. Let w = the wages earned.

Step 5 Write an equation and solve for $h = 16$, the number of hours Mike worked this week.

$w = 6h = 6 • 16$
$w =$ _____

Use a graph

Data for the line $w = 6h$ is plotted on the graph at right. The horizontal axis is labeled ___ for hours worked. The vertical axis is labeled ___ for wages earned. Notice that the line extends beyond $h = 16$ hours. You can use the graph to determine how much Mike earns. In 20 hours, he earns _____. In 24 hours, he earns _____.

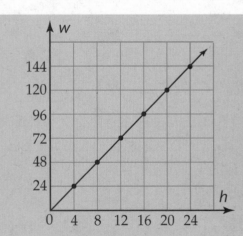

🔑 Practice

1 Which is another way to express that Angela earns $5 per hour?

A a graph of Angela's earnings versus hours worked

C Angela earned $60 working 10 hours this week.

B a table of Angela's savings each week

D a graph comparing her salary to the tips she earned

2 If *x* represents an odd number, which expression would represent the next odd number following *x* in a series of numbers?

F $x + y$ **G** $x + 1$ **H** $x - 2$ **J** $x + 2$

3 Lydia had $40. She bought 3 plants and a toothbrush. What expression shows how much money Lydia has left?

A $40 + 3x + y$ **B** $(40 - 3x) + y$ **C** $\frac{40}{x + y}$ **D** $40 - (3x + y)$

4 Which expression would you use to find the number of ounces in *m* pounds?

F $16 - m$ **G** $16 + m$ **H** $16m$ **J** $16 \div m$

5 This inequality is equivalent to which of the following statements?

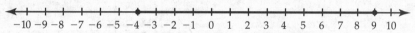

A It takes anywhere from 4 to 9 weeks for the gift to arrive.

B The weight of a cat is between 4 pounds and 9 pounds.

C The temperature was at least −4°C and at most 9°C.

D In the last 14 days, it rained every day.

6 Which of these expressions does *not* express the number 144 if *b* = 12?

F $b \cdot b$ **G** $b \cdot (-b)$ **H** $4(3b)$ **J** $12b$

7 Which of these expressions represents the number 17.5 if *x* = 4?

A $4x \div 1.5$ **B** $4x - 1.5$ **C** $4x(1.5)$ **D** $4x + 1.5$

Short-Response Question

8 Six months ago, Carly celebrated a birthday. What expression can you write to show how many months old Carly is? Explain your answer.

_____

_____

_____

> **READY REFERENCE**
>
> **relation** a set of ordered pairs
>
> **domain** the set of all first coordinates, or x-values, from the ordered pairs in a relation
>
> **range** the set of all second coordinates, or y-values, from the ordered pairs in a relation
>
> An example of a relation is the set of ordered pairs $\{(-1, -10), (0, -6), (1, -2), (2, 2), (3, 6), (4, 10)\}$. The domain for this relation is the set of all x-values $\{-1, 0, 1, 2, 3, 4\}$. The range for this relation is the set of all y-values $\{-10, -6, -2, 2, 6, 10\}$.

Think About It

How can you find the domain and range for each relation?

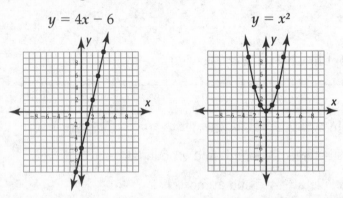

$$y = 4x - 6 \qquad y = x^2$$

Here's How

To find the domain and range for $y = 4x - 6$:

Step 1 Name some ordered pairs that satisfy $y = 4x - 6$. From the graph of $y = 4x - 6$, you can see that some of the ordered pairs that satisfy this relation include those in the set $\{(-1, -10), (0, -6), (1, -2), (2, 2), (3, 6), (4, 10)\}$. However, the linear relation $y = 4x - 6$ has infinitely many ordered pairs that satisfy.

Step 2 Identify the domain and range. There are no restrictions, so the domain is the entire set of real numbers; the range is the entire set of real numbers.

To find the domain and range for $y = x^2$:

Step 1 Name some ordered pairs that satisfy $y = x^2$. From the graph of $y = x^2$, you can see that some of the ordered pairs that satisfy this relation include those in the set $\{(-3, 9), (-2, 4), (-1, 1), (0, 0), (1, 1), (2, 4), (3, 9)\}$. However, the nonlinear relation $y = x^2$ has infinitely many ordered pairs that satisfy it.

Step 2 Identify the domain and range. Note that the graph (a parabola) has one point on the x-axis and then is always above the x-axis. There are no negative y-values. So the range is $y \geq 0$. There are no restrictions on the domain; so the domain is the entire set of real numbers.

Practice

1 Which set is the domain for the relation {(2, 4), (3, 6), (4, 8), (5, 10)}?

    A {2, 3, 4, 5}   **B** {4, 6, 8, 10}   **C** {2, 6, 8, 10}   **D** {2, 3, 4, 5, 6, 8, 10}

2 Which set is the range for the relation {(2, 4), (3, 6), (4, 8), (5, 10)}?

    F {2, 3, 4, 5}   **G** {4, 6, 8, 10}   **H** {2, 6, 8, 10}   **J** {2, 3, 4, 5, 6, 8, 10}

Use the following table of values for questions 3–5.

x	y
0	−4
1	−1
2	2
3	5
4	8

3 Which set is the domain for the relation shown in this table of values?

    A {−4, −1, 2, 5, 8}   **B** {0, −4, 1, −1, 2}   **C** {0, 1, 2, 3, 4}   **D** {−4, 1, −1, 2, 5}

4 Which set is the range for the relation?

    F {−4, −1, 2, 5, 8}   **G** {0, −4, 1, −1, 2}   **H** {0, 1, 2, 3, 4}   **J** {−4, 1, −1, 2, 5}

5 Which equation represents a relation that includes among its ordered pairs all of those that are listed in the table of values?

    A $y = 3x + 4$ **B** $y = 2x − 6$ **C** $y = 3x + 7$ **D** $y = 3x − 4$

6 What are the domain and range for the linear relation $y = −2x + 1$?

$y = −2x + 1$

    F domain = {−2, −1, 0, 1, 2}, range = {5, 3, 1, −1, −3}

    G domain = {1, 2, 3, 4, 5}, range = {2, 4, 6, 8, 10}

    H domain = {real numbers}, range = {real numbers}

    J domain = {3, 6, 0, 1, −3}, range = {−5, −11, 1, −1, 7}

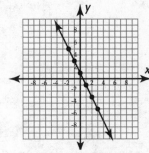

Short Response Question

$x = −y^2$

7 What are the domain and range for the relation $x = −y^2$?

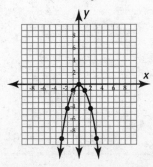

_____

Performance indicators: **8.A.18, 8.CM.3, 8.CN.2, 8.R.11**

READY REFERENCE

relation a set of ordered pairs

domain the set of all first coordinates or *x*-values from the ordered pairs
  in a relation

function a relation in which each value of the domain is associated with only
  one value in the range

range the set of all second coordinates or *y*-values from the ordered pairs
  in a relation

 Think About It

In order for a relation to be a function, each element of the domain must be paired with exactly one element of the range. (If two elements of the domain are paired with the same element of the range, the relation is still a function.) Given a table of values for a relation, how can you graph the values and determine if the relation is a function?

 Here's How

Begin with the relation $x = y^2$.

Step 1 Complete the table of values for the relation $x = y^2$.

x	y
	-3
	-2
	-1
	1
	2
	3

Step 2 Plot the ordered pairs (points) on the coordinate plane.

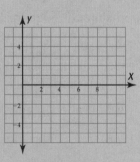

Step 3 Connect the points and label the graph $x = y^2$.

Step 4 Look at the *x*-values. Is each *x*-value paired with *exactly* one *y*-value?

_____

Is this relation a function? _____

Step 5 Another test for a function is the vertical line test. If any vertical line passes through only one point of a graph, then the graph represents a function. Does the graph of $x = y^2$ pass the vertical line test? _____

Practice

1 Which relation is *not* a function?

   A {(3, 1), (2, 2), (1, 3), (0, 4)}

   B {(7, 6), (6, 5), (5, 4), (4, 3)}

   C {(10, 5), (10, 3), (8, 2), (6, 1)}

   D {(3, 0), (6, 1), (9, 2), (12, 3)}

2 Which relation is a function?

   F {(3, 0), (5, 1), (3, 2), (9, 3)}

   G {(−8, −4), (−6, −2), (−6, 0), (−4, 2)}

   H {(2, −1), (1, 0), (0, −1), (1, −2)}

   J {(4, −2), (5, −1), (6, 0), (7, 1)}

3 Which table of values represents a function?

A

x	−1	−2	−3	−4
y	−1	−2	−3	−4

B

x	−1	−1	0	1
y	0	−2	−5	−9

C

x	3	5	7	5
y	−1	−3	−5	−7

D

x	2	5	2	5
y	2	5	8	11

4 Which table of values *does not* represent a function?

F

x	0	3	6	9
y	−2	0	2	4

G

x	6	5	4	6
y	0	−5	−10	−15

H

x	10	12	14	16
y	0	−4	8	−12

J

x	1	2	3	4
y	1	2	3	4

5 Which graph is *not* a function?

A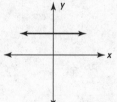

B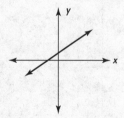

C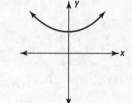

D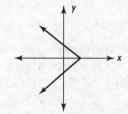

Short-Response Question

6 Is $x^2 = y$ a function? Explain your answer using a table of values.

_____

_____

_____

> **READY REFERENCE**
>
> $f(x)$ function of x; may also be used in place of y in equation where y is a function of x
>
> **function** a relation in which each value of the domain is associated with only one value of the range;
>
> *examples of functions:*
>
> $y = 3x + 9$ $\qquad$ $f(x) = 2x - 8$ $\qquad$ $y = x^2 - 7$ $\qquad$ $f(x) = x^2 - 3$

 Think About It

A problem situation that can be solved using a function may be represented with an equation, a table of values, and a graph. How do you interpret multiple representations to determine which one will help you most in solving the problem?

 Here's How

Trey belongs to a web site advertising program. After paying a monthly fee of $1, he earns $2 for each ad he sells on his web site. What is Trey's income for a month during which he sells three ads? Twenty-five ads? Is the relationship between number of ads sold and monthly income linear or nonlinear?

Step 1 Use a function to represent the situation. Trey's monthly total will be two times the number of ads he sells minus the one dollar monthly fee. The function to represent this situation is $f(x) = 2x - 1$.

Step 2 Represent the situation using the equation $y = 2x - 1$.

Step 3 Use the equation to create a table of values.

x	$2x - 1$	y
		7
3	$6 - 1$	5
2		
		1

Step 4 Graph the equation on the coordinate plane.

Step 5 Determine which representation will help you most in solving the problem.

Monthly bill for three videos: It is easy to look up the entry for 3 in the table of values and see that Trey's monthly income is $5.

Monthly bill for twenty-five videos: The table of values does not contain entries up to 25. It is easier to solve the equation for $x = 25$ to find that Trey's monthly income is $49.

Linear or nonlinear relationship: Look at the graph. It is easy to see that there is a linear relationship between number of ads sold and monthly income.

Note: You can check your solution to a problem using a different representation of the problem situation. For example, if you used a table of values to solve a problem, check your answer using an equation or a graph.

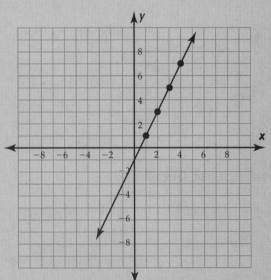

 **Practice**

Answer questions 1 and 2 using the graph below.

1 Which table of values corresponds to the graph?

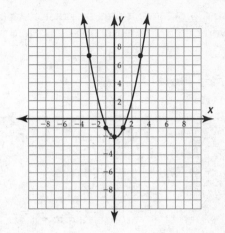

A			B			C			D	
x	$f(x)$		x	$f(x)$		x	$f(x)$		x	$f(x)$
-3	6		-3	7		-3	7		-3	9
-2	4		-2	2		-2	2		-2	4
-1	1		-1	-1		-1	1		-1	1
0	0		0	-2		0	-2		0	0
1	-1		1	-1		1	-1		1	1
2	4		2	2		2	2		2	4
3	6		3	7		3	7		3	9

2 Which function corresponds to the graph?

F $f(x) = x^2 - 2$ **H** $f(x) = x^2 + 2$

G $f(x) = x^2$ **J** $f(x) = -x$

3 Which function corresponds to
the table of values?

A $f(x) = \frac{1}{3}x$

B $f(x) = x^2$

C $f(x) = -2x + 3$

D $f(x) = -3x$

x	$f(x)$
-3	9
-2	4
-1	1
0	0
1	1
2	4
3	9

4 Which function corresponds to
the table of values?

F $f(x) = -\frac{1}{2}x$

G $f(x) = -x$

H $f(x) = -2x$

J $f(x) = -x^2$

x	$f(x)$
-3	3
-2	2
-1	1
0	0
1	-1
2	-2
3	-3

5 Which function corresponds to
the table of values?

A $f(x) = 2x + 2$

B $f(x) = x^2$

C $f(x) = -2x + 2$

D $f(x) = -3x + 3$

x	$f(x)$
-3	8
-2	6
-1	4
0	2
1	0
2	-2
3	-4

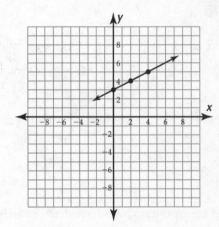

Short–Response Question

6 Write the equation represented by the graph on the
right and describe a problem-solving situation in which
the equation will help you more than the graph.

_____

_____

Think About It

When solving problems, it may be possible to anticipate limits and set expectations for solutions. How can you determine reasonable limits and expectations when solving problems?

Here's How

The perimeter P of a square is a function of the length L of one side. At a tile store, perimeters are calculated in inches for square tiles up to one square foot. If $P = 4 \times L$, what are reasonable limits for the domain and range of this situation? (Hint: One square foot has side length of one foot; one foot equals 12 inches.)

Step 1 Determine reasonable limits for the domain. The domain in this situation is the side length L (in inches) of the square tile. The side length cannot be less than or equal to zero, nor can it exceed 12 inches. A reasonable limit for the domain is $0 < L \leq 12$.

Step 2 Determine reasonable limits for the range. The range in this situation is the perimeter P (in inches) of the square tile. The perimeter cannot be less than or equal to zero inches, nor can it exceed 4×12 or 48 inches. A reasonable limit for the domain is $0 < P \leq 48$.

Practice

1 A museum is open 7 days per week. The attendance rate is 50 to 250 visitors each day. How many visitors can the museum expect each week?

A 50 to 1,750   **B** 350 to 1,000   **C** 350 to 1,750   **D** 350 to 2,500

2 A trucker drives no more than 55 miles per hour. If the trucker drives up to 10 hours each day, what is the upper limit for the number of miles the trucker can drive in 5 days?

F 550 miles   **G** 2,750 miles   **H** 5,000 miles   **J** 5,500 miles

3 The entire eighth grade class is taking a field trip to the zoo. Admission tickets are $3 each. Up to 120 students will go on the trip. What is the most money that will be spent on admission tickets?

A $120   **B** $320   **C** $360   **D** $420

4 Tariq spent over $50 buying CDs and DVDs. The price of a DVD is $5 more than a CD. Which value is *not* a possible solution for the number of CDs Tariq bought?

F −3   **G** 2   **H** 5   **J** 10

5 A cashier earns $8 per hour, working up to 8 hours each weekday. If weekly earnings e are a function of hours h worked, what are reasonable limits for the domain and range of this situation?

A domain: $0 \leq h \leq 7$; range: $0 \leq e \leq 64$ **C** domain: $0 \leq h \leq 40$; range: $0 \leq e \leq 64$

B domain: $0 \leq h \leq 8$; range: $0 \leq e \leq 64$ **D** domain: $0 \leq h \leq 40$; range: $0 \leq e \leq 320$

6 Sheila bought a case of 24 water bottles. If she drinks 2 or 3 bottles each day, how many bottles could be left in the case after a week?

F 0 to 3   **G** 0 to 10   **H** 3 to 10   **J** 8 to 12

7 A doctor sees between 20 and 30 patients each day, five days per week. Which choice is *not* a reasonable estimate of the number of patients seen in one week?

A 100 patients   **B** 112 patients   **C** 125 patients   **D** 200 patients

Short-Response Question

8 For two weeks, Jan practices the piano the same amount of minutes each day. She practices at least 35 minutes and no more than 90 minutes each day. If total practice minutes t are a function of daily practice minutes d, what are reasonable limits for the domain and range of this situation?

_____

_____

_____

_____

_____

_____

_____

Lesson 30 **Focusing on Reasoning and Proof: Develop, Explain, and Verify an Argument Using Mathematical Ideas and Language**

Performance indicators: **8.RP.5, 8.A.15**

> **READY REFERENCE**
> **profit** the difference between money earned (income) and expenses

Think About It

As you work to find solutions, be sure to include explanations that help support your reasoning. How can mathematical ideas and language support an argument that a particular solution is correct?

Here's How

Over the summer, Ben earns money mowing lawns. For each lawn, he earns $35 and spends $7 for gas. In addition, Ben has a one-time expense of $400 for the purchase of a lawn mower.

Ben uses the equation $p = 28n - 400$, where p is profit and n is number of lawns mowed, to determine that he will have to mow 50 lawns to make a profit of $1,000.

How can you show that Ben's solution is correct?

Step 1 Explain how Ben developed the equation.

Ben's profit is money earned mowing lawns minus expenses of gas and $400 to purchase a lawnmower. The profit for each lawn is $35 − $7, or $28. For n lawns, $p = 28n$. In addition, Ben must also subtract the one-time $400 expense of the lawn mower, making the equation $p = 28n - 400$.

n	p
47	916
48	944
49	927
50	1,000
51	1,028
52	1,056
53	1,084

Step 2 Check the result of Ben's equation for $n = 50$.

$p = 28n - 400$
$p = 28(50) - 400$
$p = 1,400 - 400$
$p = 1,000$

Step 3 Use a different representation of the problem situation to verify the solution.

A table of values confirms Ben's solution.

Practice

1 A large toy company makes remote-control trucks that sell for $25 each. Expenses are $10 for each truck. The table of values shows the number of trucks the company would need to sell to make profits of $15,000, $75,000, and $150,000. Which equation could be used to verify the numbers in the table?

A profit = 25 × number of trucks sold

B profit = (25 − 10) × number of trucks sold

C profit = (25 + 10) × number of trucks sold

D profit = number of trucks sold ÷ (25 − 10)

Profit	Number of Trucks Sold
$15,000.00	1,000
$75,000.00	5,000
$150,000.00	10,000

Use the table to answer question 2.

Ingredient	25 People	50 People	100 People	200 People
Orange Juice	2 qt	4 qt	8 qt	16 qt
Pineapple Juice	$1\frac{1}{2}$ c	3 c	6 c	12 c
Apple Juice	1 qt	2 qt	4 qt	8 qt

2 Which equation will help you verify that the amount of pineapple juice is consistent for all groups shown?

F pineapple juice (in cups) = 0.02 × number of people

G pineapple juice (in cups) = 0.06 × number of people

H pineapple juice (in cups) = 1.5 × number of people

J pineapple juice (in cups) = 2 × number of people

Use the circle graph to answer questions 3 and 4.

3 If 50 people answered "Yes" in the situation represented by the circle graph, how many people were questioned in total?

A 75   **C** 150

B 125   **D** 200

4 Which equation represents the number of people *n* who answer "No" as a function of people *y* who answer "Yes"?

F $n = 2y$ **H** $n = 4y$

G $n = 3y$ **J** $n = 75y$

Extended–Response Question

5 The Math Club is holding a car wash to raise money. Students raise $3 for each car they wash. In the graph below, the *x*-axis represents the number of cars washed and the *y*-axis represents the amount of money raised.

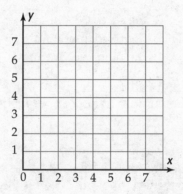

Part A Write an equation to describe the situation. Let *x* be number of cars washed and *y* be the amount of money raised.

_____

Part B Create a table of values to represent money raised. Include entries for 0 to 6 cars. Let *x* be number of cars washed and *y* be the amount of money raised.

Performance indicators: **8.CM.10, 8.A.17**

READY REFERENCE

relation a set of ordered pairs

domain the set of all first coordinates or *x*-values from the ordered pairs in a relation

range the set of all second coordinates or *y*-values from the ordered pairs in a relation

dependent variable the variable in a relation whose value depends on the value of the independent variable

independent variable the variable in a relation whose value is subject to choice

function a relation in which each value of the domain is associated with only one value in the range

---

 ## Think About It

In order to communicate mathematical ideas clearly and thoroughly, you must use appropriate language and terminology.

 ## Here's How

Some mathematical terminology is easy to confuse. By becoming aware of terminology that is often misused, you can prevent errors.

Example 1: Lucy reads 15 pages per hour. She writes the equation $p = 15h$ to describe how many pages p she will read in h hours. In this situation, Lucy identifies the pages p as the **domain** and the hours h as the **range**. She has made the common error of switching the two terms.

The domain is associated with the independent variable. This is the variable that is subject to choice. In this situation, the independent variable is the number of hours Lucy reads. The term domain is used to identify the set of values for the number of hours Lucy reads.

The range is associated with the dependent variable. This is the variable whose value depends on the value of the independent variable. In this situation, the total number of pages Lucy reads is dependent on the number of hours she reads. The term range is used to identify the set of values for the total number of pages Lucy reads.

Example 2: John refers to the equation $x = y^2$ as a **function**. He has made the common error of misusing this term.

A function is a specific type of equation in which each *x*-value is associated with only one *y*-value. In this equation, the *x*-value 4 is associated with the *y*-value 2. But the *x*-value 4 is also associated with the *y*-value -2. In fact, all positive *x*-values are associated with both positive and negative *y*-values. Therefore, it would be incorrect to refer to this equation as a function.

Measuring Up® to the New York State Learning Standards

Practice

1 Which set is the range for the relation {(3,7), (4, 8), (5, 9)}?

    A {37, 48, 59}   **B** {3, 7, 4, 8, 5, 9}   **C** {7, 8, 9}   **D** {3, 4, 5}

2 Lynn bought some pencils that cost $0.39 each and one three-ring binder for $1.19. The equation to find the total amount t of her purchase is $t = 0.39\,n + 1.19$, where n is the number of pencils she buys. What is the domain in this situation?

    F The set of values for the number of pencils Lynn buys

    G The total amount of money Lynn spends

    H The cost of one pencil

    J The cost of the three-ringer binder

3 Which equation is *not* a function?

    A $y = 3x + 2$ **B** $x = -y^2$ **C** $y = 2x^2 - 1$ **D** $y = -x$

4 Which relation is a function?

    F {(4, 2), (4, 5), (4, 0), (4, −1)}   **G** {(0, 0) (1, 1), (2, 2), (1, −1)}

    H {(1, 1), (2, 4), (3, 9), (4, 16)}   **J** {(1, 2), (2, 4), (3, 6), (4, 8)}

5 Scott orders DVDs by mail. Each DVD costs $15. Scott creates a table of values showing that 2 DVDs will cost $30, 3 DVDs will cost $45, and 4 DVDs will cost $60. What is the range of the relation represented in Scott's table of values?

    A {3}   **B** {15}   **C** {2, 3, 4}   **D** {30, 45, 60}

6 Which set is the domain for the relation {(13,17), (2, 10), (3, 10), (0, 17)}?

    F {0}   **G** {10, 17}   **H** {13, 2, 3}   **J** {13, 2, 3, 0}

7 Angela scored 75, 80, 90, and 100 on her first four spelling tests. She uses the relation {(1, 75), (2, 80), (3, 90), (4, 100)} to represent the four tests. Which statement is correct?

    A The domain for this relation is {1, 2, 3, 4}.   **C** The range for this relation is {4}.

    B The domain for this relation is {75, 80, 90, 100}.   **D** The range for this relation is {1 to 4}.

Short Response

8 Is the equation $x = 2y^2$ a function? Why or why not?

_____

_____

> **READY REFERENCE**
>
> **ratio** the comparison of two numbers by division
>
> **proportion** an equation showing that two ratios are equal
>
> **cross products** in a proportion, if $\frac{a}{b} = \frac{c}{d}$, then $ad = bc$ (b and $d \neq 0$)
>
> **percent** a ratio that compares a number to 100
>
> **simplest form** a fraction for which the numerator and denominator cannot be divided by a common factor greater than 1

 Think About It

The same mathematical idea can be represented in different ways.

 Here's How

A baseball team hit a total of 256 home runs. One player hit 32 home runs. What percent of the team's home run total did he hit?

Step 1 Put the problem in the form of a proportion.

Represent the ratio of the player's hits to the total home runs hit by the team.

$$\frac{\text{player's home runs}}{\text{total home runs}} = \frac{32}{256}$$

Represent the variable n as an unknown percentage of 100.

$$\frac{n}{100}$$

Write the problem in the form of a proportion.

$$\frac{32}{256} = \frac{n}{100}$$

Step 2 Solve the proportion by using cross products.
Cross multiply and write the new expression for this equation.

$$\frac{32}{256} = \frac{n}{100} \qquad 256n = 3{,}200$$

Divide both sides of the equation by 256 to determine the value of n.
Solve the proportion to find n equals 12.5.

Step 3 Put the answer in the form of a percent.
The player hit 12.5% of the team's home runs.

Practice

1 Which ratio compares 14 backpacks out of a total of 56 backpacks, in simplest form?

A $\frac{1}{4}$ **B** $\frac{7}{2}$ **C** $\frac{24}{56}$ **D** $\frac{2}{7}$

2 Liz is making spaghetti. If 4 people will be eating, she needs 8 ounces of sauce. For 6 people, she needs 12 ounces. For 8 people, she needs16 ounces, and so on. How could she represent this situation as an equation? Let n be the number of people and s be the ounces of sauce.

F $n = 2s$ **G** $s = 2n$ **H** $s = 8n$ **J** $n = 8s$

3 Which proportion shows that 60 is 30% of a number n?

A $\frac{60}{30} = \frac{n}{100}$ **B** $\frac{n}{30} = \frac{60}{100}$ **C** $\frac{60}{n} = \frac{30}{100}$ **D** $\frac{60}{30} = \frac{100}{n}$

4 To calculate sale prices, a store owner uses the equation $s = p - \frac{1}{10}p$, where s is sale price and p is original price. She wants to create a table of values showing original prices and sale prices. If original prices of $130, $150, $170, and $190 are entered, what are the corresponding sale prices in the table of values?

F $13, $15, $17, and $190   **H** $117, $135, $153, and $171

G $65, $75, $85, and $95   **J** $130, $150, $170, and $190

5 Samantha received 32 points in her team's basketball game. Her scoring counted for 40% of her team's total. How many points did Samantha's team score?

A 60   **B** 80   **C** 100   **D** 120

6 Kevin made the graph below to show how many miles he can walk in x hours. The x-axis is hours, the y-axis is miles walked. Which equation could also be used to describe the miles that Kevin can walk?

F $y = 1.5x$ **H** $y = 5x$

G $y = 3x$ **J** $y = x + 2$

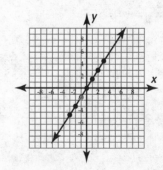

Short–Response Question

7 The equation $c = 2.5 \times n$ represents how many cans c of dog food Fido eats in n days. Create a table of values to show how many cans of dog food Fido will eat in one week, two weeks, three weeks, and four weeks. (Hint: One week equals seven days.)

READY REFERENCE

algebraic expression a variable by itself, or a combination of variables, numbers, and operations

equation a statement that two expressions are equal

solution a value that can be substituted for a variable to make an equation true

---

 Think About It

You can model an equation to find the value of a variable that is the solution to an equation. You can also use a geometric model to represent an expression.

 Here's How

The expression on the left side of the balance is $3x + 1$. The number 16 is on the right side of the balance. What value of x makes $3x + 1$ equal to 16?

$$3x + 1 = 16$$

Use the balancer to write an equation.

Step 1 Write an equation to represent the amounts shown on the balance.

_____

Step 2 Remove 1 from each side of the balance and revise the equation to represent the amounts that remain.
$$3x + 1 - 1 = 16 - 1$$
$$\underline{\quad} = 15$$

Step 3 Divide each side of the equation by 3, and revise the equation to represent the amounts that remain.
$$\frac{x}{3} = \frac{15}{3}$$
$$x = \underline{\quad}$$

Use the geometric model to write an equation.

Step 1 Write an expression to represent the width of the rectangle below. _____

Step 2 Write an expression to represent the length. _____

Step 3 Now multiply the length by the width.
$$(3 + x) \cdot 6 = (3 \cdot 6) + (x \cdot 6)$$
$$(3 + x) \cdot 6 = \underline{\quad} + \underline{\quad}$$

So the expression $A = 18 + 6x$ is the equation that represents the area of the rectangle.

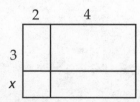

Practice

1 Which equation should be written after 1 is subtracted from both sides of the balance?

$6n + 1$ = 19

A $6n + 1 = 18$ **B** $6n = 18$ **C** $5n + 1 = 18$ **D** $5n = 18$

2 Which value of n makes $6n + 1$ equal to 19?

F 2   **G** 3   **H** 3.5   **J** 4

3 Which equation should be written after 3 is added to both sides of the balance?

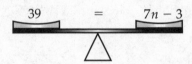

39 = $7n - 3$

A $42 = 7n$ **B** $36 = 7n$ **C** $38 = 6n$ **D** $39 = 6n$

4 Which value of n makes 39 equal to $7n - 3$?

F 3   **G** 4   **H** 5   **J** 6

5 Which equation represents the area of the figure shown below?

A $14 + 5x$

B $14 + 28x$

C $14 + 20x$

D $14 + 7x$

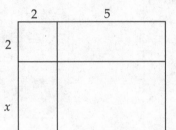

6 If the area of the figure shown above is 35, what is the value of x?

F 4.2   **G** 3   **H** 1.05   **J** 0.75

Short-Response Question

7 Use the diagram to solve the problem.

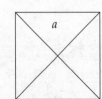

If $a = 2$, write an expression for the area of the square. Explain your answer.

_____

_____

Directions

Use a separate sheet of paper to show your work.

1 Which expression matches this word phrase?
10 plus −33 divided by a number

A $-33 + \frac{n}{10}$

B $n + \frac{-33}{10}$

C $\frac{-33}{n} + 10$

D $\frac{n}{-33} + 10$

2 Which word sentence matches this equation?
$19 \cdot x = 236$

F A rectangular room with an area of 236 square feet is 19 feet wide.

G Mrs. Glass's 19 students each sold 236 bars of candy.

H In order to win a prize, a student must read at least 19 of 236 books on a special list.

J The Jones family has traveled 19 miles of a 236 mile trip.

3 Which of the following correctly graphs the equation $3y - x = 6$?

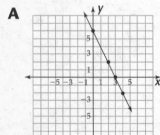

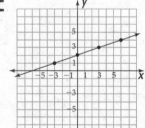

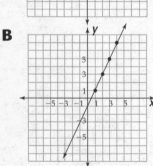

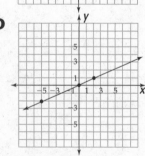

4 Which is the *least* true value for the following inequality? $7x - 3 > 39$

F 5

G 6

H 7

J 8

5 Three of the ordered pairs are solutions of the same linear equation. Which one is *not*?

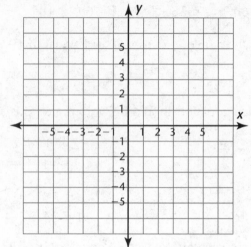

A (−2, −3)

C (2, 0)

B (−1, −1)

D (0, 1)

Use this model to answer question 6.

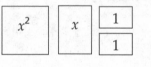

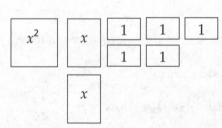

6 Look at the model. Which expression does it represent?

F $(2x^2 + 2x^2 + 6) - (x^2 + 2x - 5)$

G $(2x^2 + 4x + 5) - (x^2 + 2x^2 + 5)$

H $(2x^2 + 2x + 6) - (x^2 + 2x + 5)$

J $(x^2 - 2x - 5) - (2x^2 + x - 6)$

7 What is the product of this expression?
$(2y^8)(-16y^3)$

   A $-18y^5$ **C** $32y^{11}$

   B $18y^5$ **D** $-32y^{11}$

8 What is the product of this expression?
$(9b - 2d) \cdot c$

   F $9bc + 2cd$ **H** $9bc + 2d$

   G $9bc - 2d$ **J** $9bc - 2cd$

9 What is the sum of this expression?
$(32x + 19) + (17x - 22)$

   A $49x - 3$ **C** $15x + 41$

   B $49x - 41$ **D** $15x - 3$

10 What is the quotient of this expression?
$(18x^2 + 12x - 27) \div 3x$

   F $6x^2 + 12x - 3$

   G $6x^2 + 12x - 3x$

   H $6x + 4 - \frac{9}{x}$

   J $\frac{6x + 4}{x} - \frac{9}{x}$

11 What are the factors of $x^2 + 10x + 16$?
Complete the table to help you answer
the question.

Factors of ___	Sum of Factors
1,16	

   A $(x + 4)(x + 4)$

   B $(x + 2)(x + 4)$

   C $(x + 8)(x + 2)$

   D $(x + 4)(x + 8)$

12 What is the solution of this inequality?
$12x \div 4 < 81$

   F $x > 27.0625$ **H** $x < 5.0625$

   G $x < 27$ **J** $x > 5$

Use this figure to answer questions 13–14.

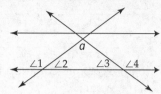

13 If $m\angle 2 = m\angle 3$ and $m\angle 4$ is 125°, which
expression can be used to find $m\angle 2$?

   A $180° - 55°$ **C** $125° + 180°$

   B $180° + 55°$ **D** $180° - 125°$

14 What is the measure of $\angle 2$?

   F   90°   **H**   55°

   G   60°   **J**   50°

15 Which inequality is shown on this number line?

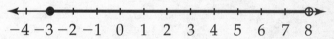

   A $-3 < x < 8$ **C** $3 \leq x < -8$

   B $-3 < x \leq 8$ **D** $-3 \leq x < 8$

16 If $x = -4$, which inequality is true?

   F $\frac{-2}{x} + x \leq x^3$

   G $x \cdot -2 \geq 2x^2 + x$

   H $\frac{x}{2} < x^2 + 4x$

   J $x - 2 \geq x^2 + 4x$

17 Cycle King Bicycles is planning to restock their mountain bikes. The wholesale cost is $210 for each of the first 10 bikes they buy. For additional bikes, the price of each bike drops to $150.

Part A Write a word equation to show the total cost c of buying *x* bikes where *x* > 10.

_____

_____

Part B Write an algebraic equation that matches your word equation.

_____

_____

Part C Cycle King Bicycles decides to buy 15 bikes. Simplify your algebraic equation and then solve it to find the wholesale cost. Show all work.

_____

_____

_____

_____

_____

18 Celia is taking up skiing but she can't decide whether to buy the equipment or to rent it. If she rents the equipment, she will pay $75.00 for each ski trip. If she buys the equipment for $200.00, she will pay $25.00 for each trip. For what number of trips would each option cost the same amount?

Let x = the number of trips. Let y = total cost.

Part A Write an equation that shows the total cost if she rents the equipment.

Write an equation that shows the total cost if she buys the equipment.

Part B Make a table below. Have a column for x and a column for each equation. Fill in the table showing three solutions for each.

Part C Find an algebraic solution. Show your work.

Part D Graph each equation on the coordinate plane and find the point where they intersect.

After how many trips will the total cost be the same? _____

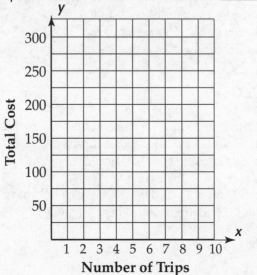

Performance indicators: **8.G.0, 8.R.2**

READY REFERENCE

congruent figures that have the same size and shape; the symbol ≅ means
   is congruent to

angle a figure formed by two rays that have a common endpoint

---

 Think About It

You can use tools such as compasses and straight edges to construct geometric figures.
To construct angles and bisectors, follow the steps below.

 Here's How

Construct ∠ABC congruent to ∠XYZ.

Step 1 You are given ∠XYZ. To construct ∠ABC, start by drawing a ray.
   Label the endpoint B.

Step 2 Place the compass tip at Y and draw an arc that intersects
   both $\overrightarrow{YX}$ and $\overrightarrow{YZ}$.

Step 3 Keep the compass open to the same width. Place the tip at B. Draw
   an arc intersecting the ray at point C. Notice that $\overline{BC}$ and the line
   segment including Y and the point where the arc intersects $\overrightarrow{YZ}$ and
   the line segment $\overline{BC}$ are congruent line segments.

Step 4 Adjust the compass width so that the tip and the pencil are at the
   points where the arc intersects $\overrightarrow{YX}$ and $\overrightarrow{YZ}$.

Step 5 Keeping the same compass width, place the tip at C and draw an
   arc that intersects the first arc. Label the point of the intersection A.
   Draw $\overrightarrow{BA}$.
   ∠ABC ≅ ∠XYZ

Construct the angle bisector of ∠M.

Step 1 You are given ∠M. To bisect this angle, start by making an arc.
   Put the tip of the compass at M and draw an arc that intersects
   the sides of ∠M. Label the points of intersection Q and R.

Step 2 With the compass tip at Q and then at R, and with the same compass
   opening, draw intersecting arcs. Label the point where the arcs intersect N.

Step 3 Draw $\overrightarrow{MN}$. $\overrightarrow{MN}$ is the bisector of ∠QMR.
   ∠QMN ≅ ∠ _____

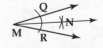

Construct the perpendicular bisector of $\overline{AB}$.

Step 1 You are given $\overline{AB}$. Open the compass to more than half the length of $\overline{AB}$. Place the tip of the compass at A and draw an arc intersecting $\overline{AB}$.

Step 2 Keep the compass open to the same width. Place the tip at B and draw another arc intersecting $\overline{AB}$. Label the points of intersection of the arcs C and D.

Step 3 Draw $\overline{CD}$. Label the intersection of $\overline{AB}$ and $\overline{CD}$ point M. $\overline{CD}$ is the perpendicular bisector of $\overline{AB}$. Point M is the midpoint of _____

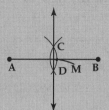

🔑 Practice

1 In the figure shown, what kind of construction is shown?

A a perpendicular bisector

B a congruent angle

C bisecting an angle

D bisecting a line

2 In the figure shown, what is the perpendicular bisector of $\overleftrightarrow{CD}$?

F M **H** $\overrightarrow{MD}$

G $\overrightarrow{MC}$ **J** $\overleftrightarrow{QR}$

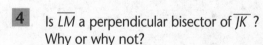

3 Which of the following explains why $\overrightarrow{BD}$ in the figure shown is not an angle bisector?

A The resulting angles are not congruent.

B The resulting angles do not form right angles.

C The resulting angles are congruent.

D The resulting angles are not perpendicular to the original angle.

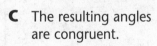

4 Is $\overline{LM}$ a perpendicular bisector of $\overline{JK}$? Why or why not?

F Yes, because it is perpendicular to $\overline{JK}$.

G No, because it does not divide $\overline{LM}$ into two congruent parts.

H No, because it is not perpendicular to $\overline{JK}$.

J Yes, because it is perpendicukar to $\overline{JK}$ and it divides $\overline{JK}$ into two congruent parts.

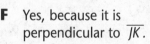
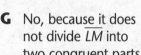

Short-Response Question

5 Construct a line segment congruent to $\overline{AB}$. Explain your procedure.

_____

_____

_____

Performance indicators: **8.G.1, 8.RP.3, 8.R.8**

READY REFERENCE

adjacent angles angles with the same vertex and a common side

straight angle an angle formed by two opposing rays

congruent figures that have the same size and shape; the symbol ≅ means
is congruent to

 Think About It

Vertical angles are the opposite angles formed by two intersecting lines. Vertical angles are congruent.

 Here's How

Determine why vertical angles are congruent.

Step 1 Opposite rays form a straight angle with a measure of 180°.

Step 2 Draw a line that goes through the end point shared by the rays. Look at the angles formed. Let *A*, *B*, *C* and *D* stand for the measures of the four angles.

Step 3 Since each pair of adjacent angles forms a straight angle with a measure of 180°, the following equations occur:

$A + B = 180°$ $B + C = 180°$

$C + D = 180°$ $D + A = 180°$

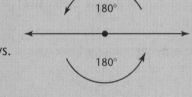

Step 4 By subtraction, it can be shown that:

$$\begin{aligned} A + B &= 180° \\ -(B + C &= 180°) \\ \hline A - C &= 0 \\ A &= C \end{aligned} \qquad \begin{aligned} B + C &= 180° \\ -(C + D &= 180°) \\ \hline B - D &= 0 \\ B &= D \end{aligned}$$

Since *A* = *C* and *B* = *D*, each pair of vertical angles has the same measure. Therefore, vertical angles are congruent.

Identify pairs of vertical angles as congruent.

Step 1 What angle is congruent to angle *P*? _____

Step 2 What angle is congruent to angle *S*? _____

Step 3 Let angle *Q* have a measure of 45° and angle *R* have a measure of 135°. What is the measure of angle *S*? _____

Step 4 What is the measure of angle *P*? _____

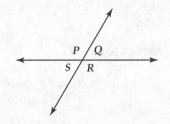

Practice

Use the figure below to answer questions 1–4.

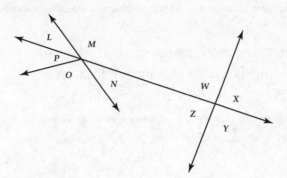

1 What angle is congruent to ∠L?

 A ∠M   **C** ∠O

 B ∠N   **D** ∠W

2 What angle is congruent to ∠Z?

 F ∠W   **H** ∠Y

 G ∠X   **J** ∠O

3 If the measure of ∠M is 119° and the measure of ∠P is 30°, what is the measure of ∠O?

 A 31°   **C** 150°

 B 61°   **D** 180°

4 If the measure of ∠Y is 92°, what is the measure of ∠W?

 F 88°   **H** 92°

 G 90°   **J** 180°

Short-Response Question

5 Consider a pair of scissors. If you open the scissors to the point where the handle parts of the scissors are open at an angle of 57°, at what angle are the scissors open at on the cutting end?

_____

Say that y is equal to the measure of the angle at which the handle part is open. Also, x is equal to the measure of the angle at which the cutting end of the scissors is open. What equation could be applied to this situation with the variables x and y?

_____

READY REFERENCE

adjacent angles angles with the same vertex and a common side
supplementary angles two angles whose measures add to 180°
complementary angles two angles whose measures add to 90°

🔑 Think About It

The angle measure of a straight angle is 180°, so any two adjacent angles that form a straight angle are supplementary angles. The angle measure of a right angle is 90°, so any two adjacent angles that form a right angle are complementary angles. Only two angles can be supplementary or complementary. Note, however, that supplementary and complementary angles do not have to be adjacent angles.

🔑 Here's How

Identify pairs of supplementary angles.

Step 1 ∠A and ∠B form a straight angle.
What is the sum of the measures of angles
∠A and ∠B? _____

Step 2 Are ∠A and ∠B supplementary? _____

Identify pairs of complementary angles.

Step 1 What is the sum of the measures of ∠J and ∠K? _____

Step 2 Are ∠J and ∠K complementary? _____

right angle symbol →

Step 3 Look at ∠C, ∠D, and ∠E.
Are these angles supplementary. _____
Why not? _____

Step 4 You are given that ∠F ≅ ∠A and ∠G ≅ ∠B.
Do the measures of ∠F and ∠G add to 180°? _____
Are these angles supplementary? _____
Why? _____
_____

Practice

Use the figures below to answer questions 1–6.

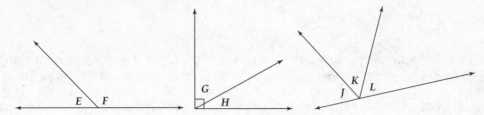

1 Which term *best* describes the relationship between ∠J and ∠K?

A adjacent angles

B complementary angles

C supplementary angles

D vertical angles

2 Which term *best* describes the relationship between ∠G and ∠H?

F equal angles

G complementary angles

H supplementary angles

J vertical angles

3 What is the sum of the measures of ∠G and ∠H?

A 75°

B 90°

C 135°

D 180°

4 Which term *best* describes the relationship between ∠E and ∠F?

F equal angles

G complementary angles

H supplementary angles

J vertical angles

5 What is the sum of the measures of ∠E and ∠F?

A 60°   **C** 100°

B 90°   **D** 180°

6 Are ∠J, ∠K, and ∠L supplementary angles?

F No, the measures do not add to 180°.

G Yes, the measures add to 180°.

H No, only two angles can be supplementary.

J No, the measures add to 90°.

Short-Response Question

7 Look at the picture.

∠BA is perpendicular to ∠BC at B. ∠ABC was bisected to form ∠Y and ∠Z.

What is the sum of the measures of ∠X and ∠ABC? _____

What term *best* describes the relationship between ∠X and ∠ABC?

_____

What terms *best* describe the relationship between ∠Y and ∠Z ?

_____ and _____

Lesson 37 **Calculate the Missing Angle**

Performance indicators: **8.G.3, 8.RP.8**

Think About It

The sum of the measures of a supplementary pair of angles is 180°. Given the measure of one angle in a supplementary pair, the measure of the other angle is 180° minus the measure of the given angle.

The sum of the measures of a complementary pair of angles is 90°. Given the measure of one angle in a complementary pair, the measure of the other angle is 90° minus the measure of the given angle.

Here's How

Calculate the missing angle measure in a supplementary pair of angles.

Step 1 Look at $\angle A$ and $\angle B$, which form a straight line.

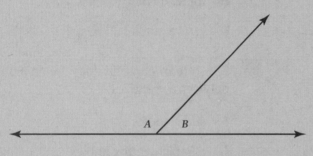

Are $\angle A$ and $\angle B$ supplementary? _____

Step 2 What is the sum of the measures of $\angle A$ and $\angle B$? _____

Step 3 If the measure of $\angle B$ is 70°, what is the measure of $\angle A$?
$m\angle A = 180° - m\angle B = 180° - 70° =$ _____

Calculate the missing angle measure in a complementary pair of angles.

Step 1 Look at the angles formed in the right angle.

Are $\angle C$ and $\angle D$ complementary angles? _____

Step 2 What is the sum of the measures of $\angle C$ and $\angle D$? _____

Step 3 If the measure of $\angle C$ is 25°, what is the measure of $\angle D$?

$m\angle D = 90° - m\angle C = 90° - 25° =$ _____

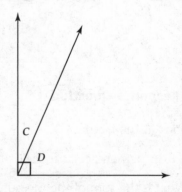

 **Practice**

Use the figures below to answer questions 1–4.

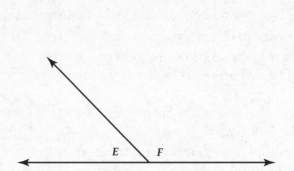

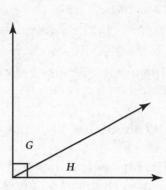

1 If the measure of ∠E is 48°, what is the measure of ∠F?

   A 42°   **C** 132°

   B 122°   **D** 142°

2 If the measure of ∠G is 57°, what is the measure of ∠H?

   F 23°   **H** 43°

   G 33°   **J** 123°

3 If the measure of ∠F is 106°, what is the measure of ∠E?

   A 64°   **C** 84°

   B 74°   **D** 164°

4 If the measure of ∠H is 19°, what is the measure of ∠G?

   F 41°   **H** 71°

   G 61°   **J** 161°

Short-Response Question

5 Look at the picture.

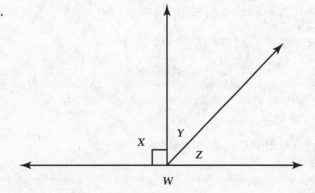

What is the sum of the measures of ∠X, ∠Y, and ∠Z? _____

What is the sum of the measures of ∠Y and ∠Z? _____

Given that ∠Y ≅ ∠Z, what is the measure of ∠Z? _____

READY REFERENCE

parallel lines lines in the same plane that always remain the same distance apart

transversal a line that intersects two or more other lines

corresponding angles a pair of angles that lie on the same side of a transversal and on the same side of the two lines cut by the transversal (∠1 and ∠7; ∠5 and ∠3)

alternate interior angles the angles on opposite sides of the transversal that are inside the parallel lines (∠5 and ∠8; ∠6 and ∠7)

alternate exterior angles the angles on opposite sides of the transversal that are outside the parallel lines (∠1 and ∠4; ∠2 and ∠3)

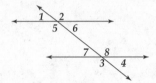

 Think About It

When any two lines are cut by a transversal, eight angles are formed. You have seen that when the lines are parallel, certain pairs of these angles are congruent. Now, you can determine why these relationships are so. To begin, you assume one relationship—based on experimentation—that when two parallel lines are cut by a transversal, corresponding angles are congruent. So, ∠A ≅ ∠C.

 Here's How

Prove that alternate interior angles are congruent.

Step 1   ∠C ≅ ∠A because corresponding angles of parallel lines are congruent.

Step 2   ∠B ≅ ∠A because vertical angles are congruent.

Step 3   ∠B ≅ ∠C because they are each congruent to _____.

Conclusion: When the lines cut by a transversal are parallel, alternate interior angles are _____.

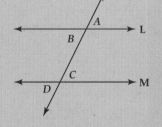

Prove that alternate exterior angles are congruent.

Step 1   ∠A ≅ ∠C because _____ angles of parallel lines are congruent.

Step 1   ∠D ≅ ∠C because _____ angles are congruent.

Step 2   ∠A ≅ ∠D because they are each congruent to ∠C.

Conclusion: When the lines cut by a transversal are parallel, _____ are congruent.

 Practice

Use the figure to answer questions 1–5.

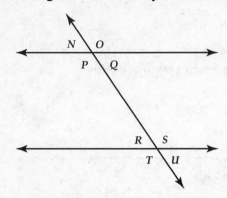

1 Which term *best* describes the relationship between ∠N and ∠Q?

A adjacent angles

B complementary angles

C supplementary angles

D vertical angles

2 Which term *best* describes the relationship between ∠O and ∠S?

F congruent angles

G complementary angles

H supplementary angles

J vertical angles

3 Which term *best* describes the relationship between ∠R and ∠U?

A adjacent angles

B congruent angles

C complementary angles

D supplementary angles

4 Which term *best* describes the relationship between ∠P and ∠R?

F congruent angles

G complementary angles

H supplementary angles

J vertical angles

5 Which term *best* describes the relationship between ∠Q and ∠T?

A equal angles

B complementary angles

C supplementary angles

D vertical angles

Short-Response Question

6 Look at the picture of a pair of parallel lines intersecting another pair of parallel lines.

What term *best* describes the relationship between ∠V and ∠W?

_____

What term *best* describes the relationship between ∠V and ∠Y?

_____

What term *best* describes the relationship between ∠V and ∠X?

_____

What term *best* describes the relationship between ∠Y and ∠Z?

_____

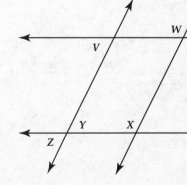

Think About It

Vertical angles have equal measures, and supplementary angles have measures that add to 180°. When a pair of parallel lines is cut by a transversal, the corresponding angles are congruent. How can you use these relationships to find the meaure of a missing angle.

 Here's How

Calculate the missing angle measurements when given one angle.

Step 1 Look at the angles formed by a transversal that cuts two parallel lines.

Step 2 What is the sum of the measures of ∠A and ∠B? _____

What is the sum of the measures of ∠A and ∠H? _____

Step 3 Are ∠B and ∠F congruent? _____

Are ∠A and ∠G congruent? _____

Step 4 If ∠D measures 60°, what is the measure of ∠C? _____

What is the measure of ∠G? _____

Step 5 If ∠E measures 108°, what is the measure of ∠G? _____

What is the measure of ∠B? _____

Step 6 If you know the measure of one angle in the diagram, can you find the measure of any of the other angles? _____

Practice

The figure below shows two parallel lines cut by a transversal. Use it to anwer questions 1–5.

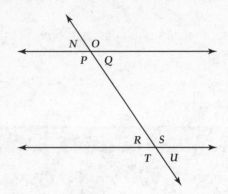

1 If the measure of ∠N is 39°, what is the measure of ∠S?

A 39°

B 51°

C 129°

D 141°

2 What is the measure of ∠T if the measure of ∠O is 117°?

F 27° **H** 117°

G 63° **J** 153°

3 If the measure of ∠P is 146°, what is the measure of ∠R?

A 34° **C** 124°

B 56° **D** 146°

4 If the measure of ∠U is 22°, what is the measure of ∠O?

F 22° **H** 112°

G 68° **J** 158°

5 What is the measure of ∠P if the measure of∠Q is 63°?

A 53° **C** 107°

B 63° **D** 117°

Short-Response Question

6 Look at the picture of two pairs of intersecting parallel lines.

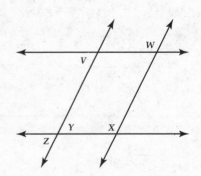

The measure of ∠V is 85°.

What is the measure of ∠W? _____

What is the measure of ∠X? _____

What is the measure of ∠Y? _____

What is the measure of ∠Z? _____

Performance indicators: **8.G.6, 8.PS.4**

Think About It

When two lines intersect, two pairs of vertical angles are formed. Also, the sum of angles that form a straight angle is 180°.

Here's How

Calculate the missing angle measurements when given two intersecting lines and an angle.

Step 1 Look at the angles formed by two intersecting lines.

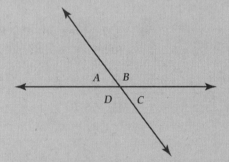

Step 2 Name two pairs of vertical angles. _____ and _____

_____ and _____

Are the measures of ∠A and ∠C equal? _____

Are the measures of ∠B and ∠D equal? _____

Step 3 Which angles are supplementary to ∠A? _____ and _____

Which angles are supplementary to ∠D? _____ and _____

What is the sum of the measures of ∠A and ∠B? _____

What is the sum of the measures of ∠B and ∠C? _____

Step 4 Suppose ∠A has a measure of 80°.

What is the measure of ∠B? _____

What is the measure of ∠C? _____

What is the measure of ∠D? _____

 **Practice**

Use the figure below to answer questions 1–5.

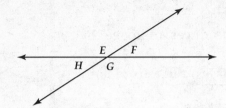

1 If the measure of ∠E is 116°, what is the measure of ∠H?

A 26° **C** 116°

B 64° **D** 154°

2 What is the measure of ∠G if the measure of ∠H is 12°?

F 12° **H** 102°

G 78° **J** 168°

3 If the measure of ∠G is 131°, what is the measure of ∠E?

A 41° **C** 131

B 49° **D** 139°

4 If the measure of ∠F is 43°, what is the measure of ∠H?

F 43° **H** 133°

G 47° **J** 137°

5 What is the measure of ∠G if the measure of ∠F is 55°?

A 35° **C** 125°

B 55° **D** 145°

Short-Response Question

6 Look at the picture of three intersecting lines.

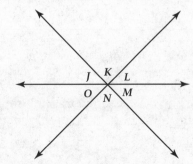

The measure of ∠J is 50° and the measure of ∠K is 60°.

What is the sum of the measures of ∠J and ∠K? _____

What is the measure of ∠L? _____

What is the measure of ∠M? _____

What is the measure of ∠N? _____

What is the measure of ∠O? _____

READY REFERENCE

transformation an operation on a geometric figure that produces an image that differs from the original figure in size, shape, or position

rotation a transformation in which a figure pivots or turns around a fixed point or line

reflection a transformation that produces the mirror image of a geometric figure

translation a transformation that moves a geometric figure by sliding each of its points the same distance in the same direction

dilation a transformation that changes the size of a figure to produce an image that is similar to the original figure

 Think About It

A change in the size, position, or shape of an object is called a transformation. Four transformations are described below.

Here's How

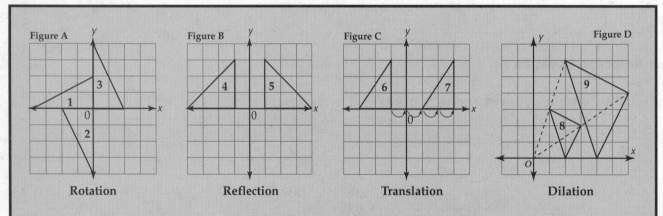

Figure A	Figure B	Figure C	Figure D
Rotation	Reflection	Translation	Dilation

1. Look at the three triangles in Figure A. Triangle 1 has gone through rotations about the origin to become Triangles 2 and 3. Triangle 2 shows Triangle 1 rotated 90° counterclockwise. Triangle 3 shows Triangle 1 rotated _____ counterclockwise.

2. In Figure B, Triangle 4 has been flipped across the *y*-axis to produce a mirror image. Triangle 5 is a reflection of Triangle 4.

3. In Figure C, Triangle 6 has changed position and become Triangle 7. Count the number of squares between the right angle of Triangle 6 and the right angle of Triangle 7. How many squares to the right did Triangle 6 move in order to be translated into Triangle 7? _____

4. In Figure D, Triangle 9 is a dilation of Triangle 8. The center of dilation in this case is the origin. It has the same shape as Triangle 8, but its size is different. In a dilation, a shape may become either larger or smaller.

Practice

Use the figures below to answer questions 1–4.

Figure E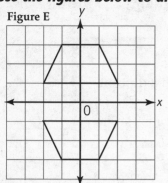

Figure F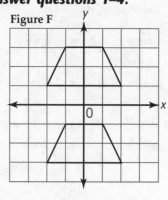

Figure G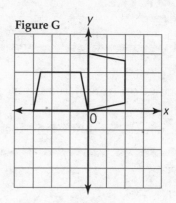

Figure H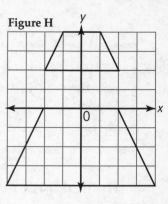

1 What is the transformation shown in Figure E?

A dilation   **C** rotation

B reflection   **D** translation

2 What is the transformation shown in Figure F?

F dilation   **H** rotation

G reflection   **J** translation

3 What is the transformation shown in Figure G?

A dilation   **C** rotation

B reflection   **D** translation

4 What is the transformation shown in Figure H?

F dilation   **H** rotation

G reflection   **J** translation

5 In which figure below has Triangle 1 been reflected *across* the *x*-axis and translated 3 units to the right?

A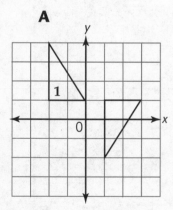

B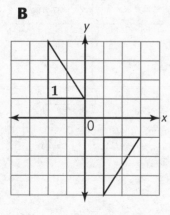

C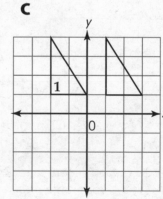

D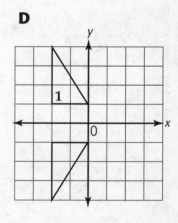

Short-Response Question

6 In a dilation, is the original figure similar to or congruent to the image? How do you know?

_____

_____

Performance indicators: **8.G.8, 8.CM.10, 8.R.5**

READY REFERENCE

rotation a transformation in which a figure pivots or turns around a fixed point or line

vertex the point at which two lines, line segments, or rays meet to form an angle

---

 Think About It

You can draw transformations in the coordinate plane. Look at the triangles in the coordinate planes to the right. Triangle 1 was rotated 90° counterclockwise (to the left) about the origin to produce the image, Triangle 2.

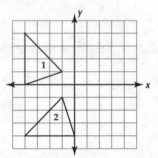

 Here's How

Draw the image of △GHI after a counterclockwise rotation of 90° about the origin.

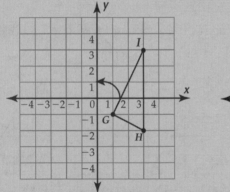 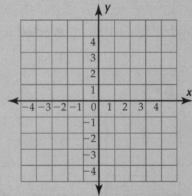

Step 1 Place a piece of tracing paper over the grid. Trace the vertices of the triangle, the *x*-axis, and the *y*-axis. Then place your pencil at the origin to rotate the paper.

Step 2 Rotate the paper 90° to the left (counterclockwise). The axes should line up. Mark the position of each vertex by pressing through the paper.

Step 3 Remove the tracing paper and complete the figure.

Step 4 After completing your figure, label the vertices in your drawing that correspond to those in the original with the same letters and a prime (') symbol. For example, you will label one vertex as *G'*, one as *H'*, and the other as *I'*. *H'* is read "*H* prime."

Practice

Use the figures below to answer questions 1–4.

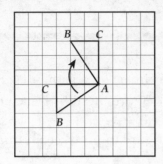

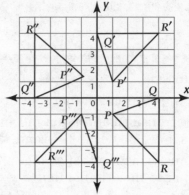

1 Which describes the rotation of △ABC around point A to form △A'B'C'?

    A 90° clockwise rotation

    B 180° clockwise rotation

    C 90° counterclockwise rotation

    D 180° counterclockwise rotation

2 The vertices for △PQR are P (1, −1), Q (4, 0), R (4, −4). Which of the images is a 90° counterclockwise rotation about the origin of △PQR?

    F △PQR

    G △P'Q'R'

    H △P"Q"R"

    J △P'''Q'''R'''

3 After △PQR is rotated 90° counterclockwise about the origin, which set of coordinates names Q'?

    A (4, 0)   **C** (−4, 0)

    B (0, 4)   **D** (0, −4)

4 Which image represents a 180° clockwise rotation of △PQR about the origin?

    F △PQR   **H** △P"Q"R"

    G △P'Q'R'   **J** △P'''Q'''R'''

Short-Response Question

5 Graph △ABC with vertices A (3, −3), B (8, −5), and C (0, −8). Draw the images formed by rotating the triangle counterclockwise 90° and 180° about the origin. List the points for each new image.

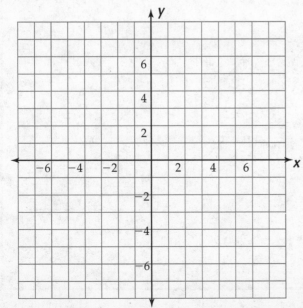

Performance indicators: **8.G.9, 8.G.10, 8.G.11, 8.R.5, 8.R.8**

READY REFERENCE

reflection a transformation that produces the mirror image of a geometric figure

translation a transformation that moves a geometric figure by sliding each of the points the same distance in the same direction

dilation a transformation that changes the size of a figure to produce an image that is similar to the original figure

---

 Think About It

Follow the steps below to draw reflections, translations, and dilations in the coordinate plane.

 Here's How

Translation

Translate △*ABC* to the left 3 units and up 2 units.

Step 1 Slide each vertex left 3 units and up 2 units.

Step 2 Connect the vertices of the image.

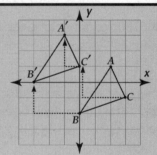

Reflection

Reflect △*DEF* over the *x*-axis.

Step 1 Since *E* is 3 units above the *x*-axis, *E'* is 3 units below the *x*-axis.

Step 2 Reflect the other vertices. Connect the vertices, draw △*D'E'F'*.

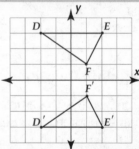

Dilation

A scale factor *f* is used to describe a dilation. For an increase in size, called an expansion, $f > 1$. For a decrease in size, called a contraction, $f < 1$. How can you find the image of △*JKL* if the dilation has a scale factor of 2 and the center of dilation is the origin?

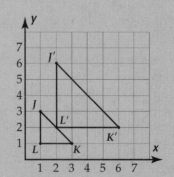

Step 1 Since the center of dilation is the origin, you can multiply the coordinates of point *J* by *f* to find the coordinates of *J'*.

J at (1, 3) → *J'* at ($f \cdot 1$, $f \cdot 3$) → *J'* at ($2 \cdot 1$, $2 \cdot 3$)

The coordinates of *J'* are _____.

Step 2 Find the coordinates of *K'* and *L'* and draw △*J'K'L'*.

Coordinates of *K'*: _____ Coordinates of *L'*: _____

🔑 Practice

Use the figures below to answer questions 1–4.

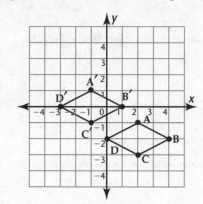

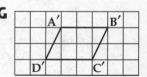

1 Look at the figure on the left. Which *best* describes the translation of this image?

A left 2 units, up 3 units

B right 3 units, down 2 units

C left 3 units, up 2 units

D left 4 units, up 3 units

2 Look at the figure on the right. Translate the figure above 3 units to the right and down 3 units. Which set of coordinates names *T'*?

F (2, 3)

G (2, −3)

H (3, −2)

J (−3, 2)

3 After the translation of the figure described in question 2, which set of coordinates names *S'*?

A (−1, −3) **B** (2, 3) **C** (3, 2) **D** (−1, 2)

4 Which shows *ABCD* changed by expansion?

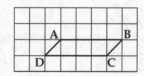

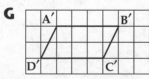 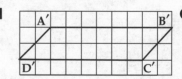

Short-Response Question

5 In Figure 1, translate △*ABC* to the right 5 units and up 3 units. In Figure 2, graph the image of △*DEF* after a reflection across the *x*-axis. In Figure 3, graph the reflection of △*JKL* across the line *y* = *x*.

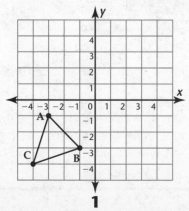 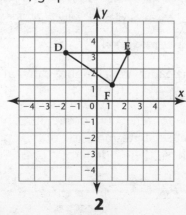 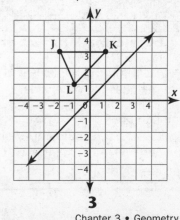

1 **2** **3**

Performance indicators: **8.G.12, 8.CN.1**

READY REFERENCE

congruent having the same shape and the same size

similar having the same shape but not necessarily the same size

symmetry a figure has a line of symmetry when the part of the figure on one side
of the line is the mirror image, or reflection, of the part on the other side

---

 Think About It

Look at the figures below. How can you determine which transformations produce similar figures and
which produce congruent figures? How can you determine which transformations preserve symmetry?

 Here's How

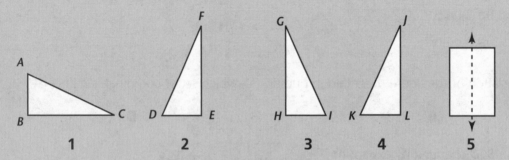

Find transformations that produce similar and congruent figures.

Compare Figure 1 to Figure 2, Figure 3, and Figure 4.

     Triangle 2 is a _____ of Triangle 1.

     Triangle 4 is a _____ of Triangle 3.

     Triangle 4 is a _____ of Triangle 1.

     Which of these transformations produce congruent angles? _____

     Which of these transformations does *not* produce congruent sides? _____

     Which of these transformations shown *always* produces congruent triangles? _____
     _____

     Which of these transformations produces similar figures? _____

Find transformations that preserve symmetry.

Trace each figure onto a sheet of tracing paper. Which figure can you fold in half so that one side of the
figure matches the other side? _____

If one half of a figure is the mirror image, or reflection, of the other half, that figure has
_____. An imaginary line that separates one side of the figure and its reflection is called
a *line of symmetry*. If a figure is symmetrical, then symmetry is preserved by a translation, rotation,
reflection, or dilation.

Measuring Up® to the New York State Learning Standards

 **Practice**

Use the figures below to answer questions 1–2.

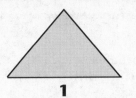 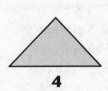

1   1   2   3   4

1 Which figures are similar but *not* congruent?

  A 1 and 2

  B 2 and 4

  C 2 and 3

  D 1 and 4

2 Which figures are congruent?

  F 1 and 2

  G 2 and 3

  H 1 and 3

  J 3 and 4

Use the figures below to answer questions 3–4.

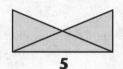 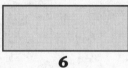 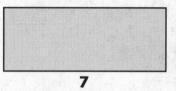 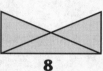

     5   6   7   8

3 Which figures are congruent?

  A 5 and 7

  B 5 and 8

  C 6 and 7

  D 6 and 8

4 Which figures are similar, but *not* congruent?

  F 6 and 7

  G 6 and 8

  H 5 and 6

  J 5 and 8

5 Which of the figures below have a line of symmetry?

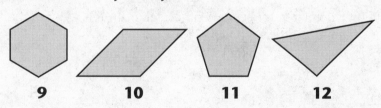

     9   10   11   12

  A 9, 10, and 11   **B** 10, 11, and 12   **C** 9, 11, and 12   **D** 9, 10, and 12

Short-Response Question

6 Which transformations will create a figure congruent to the original image? Which transformations will create a figure that is similar but *not* congruent to the original image?

_____

_____

Performance indicators: **8.G.13, 8.PS.6**

> **READY REFERENCE**
>
> **slope of a line** the ratio of the change in value of the y-coordinates
>   (the rise) to the corresponding change in the x-coordinates (the run)
>   of two points on the line
>   For any two points (x_1, y_1) and (x_2, y_2) on a line, slope $= \dfrac{\text{rise}}{\text{run}} = \dfrac{y_2 - y_1}{x_2 - x_1}$

 Think About It

How can you use a graph to find the slope of a line?

 Here's How

Step 1   Use the graph to find the coordinates of two points on the line.

The coordinates of point A
are _____ , _____ .

The coordinates of point B
are _____ , _____ .

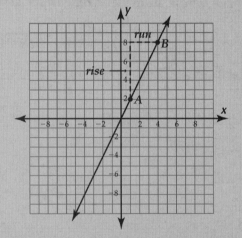

Step 2   Use the coordinates to find the ratio of the rise to the run.

The rise between the two points is
$y_2 - y_1 = 8 - 2 = $ _____ .

The run between the two points is
$x_2 - x_1 = 4 - 1 = $ _____ .

slope $= \dfrac{y_2 - y_1}{x_2 - x_1} = \dfrac{6}{3} = $ _____

So, using points A and B, the slope of the line is 2.

Step 3   Substitute the coordinates of any two other points on the line into the formula to find the slope. For example, use $(-2, -4)$ and $(3, 6)$.

slope $= \dfrac{y_2 - y_1}{x_2 - x_1} = \dfrac{6 - (-4)}{3 - (-2)} = \dfrac{}{5} = 2$

So, the slope of a line is the same (constant) for any two points on the line. Since the slope ratio represents a rate of change, then the slope of a line represents a constant rate of change.

Practice

Use the graph below to answer questions 1–5.

1 What are the coordinates of point *A*?

A (−6, 0)   **C** (−6, −2)

B (−6, −1)   **D** (−6, −3)

2 What are the coordinates of point *B*?

F (8, 3)   **H** (8, 5)

G (8, 4)   **J** (8, 6)

3 What is the change in *x*, moving from point *A* to point *B* on the line?

A 2   **C** 14

B 8   **D** 16

4 What is the change in *y*, moving from point *A* to point *B* on the line?

F 3   **H** 7

G 5   **J** 9

5 What is the slope of this line?

A −2   **B** $-\frac{1}{2}$ **C** $\frac{1}{2}$ **D** 2

Short-Response Question

6 A carnival is selling tickets at a price of 3 dollars each. The following is a graph of the revenue the carnival will receive if they sell *x* number of tickets: *y* = revenue in dollars, and *x* = number of tickets sold.

If the carnival sells 0 tickets, how much revenue will they earn? _____

If the carnival sells 3 tickets, how much revenue will they earn? _____

For each additional ticket they sell, how much more revenue will the carnival earn? _____

What is the slope of the line? _____

What is the constant rate of change, expressed with the units in the problem?

_____

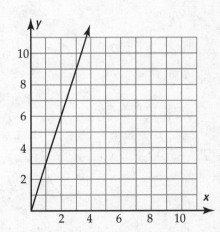

Think About It

When a line intersects the *y*-axis, the point of intersection occurs when $x = 0$. The point on the line that intersects the *y*-axis is $(0, y)$, where the value of *y* is known as the *y*-intercept. How do you locate the *y*-intercept of a line?

 Here's How

Locate the *y*-intercept of a line.

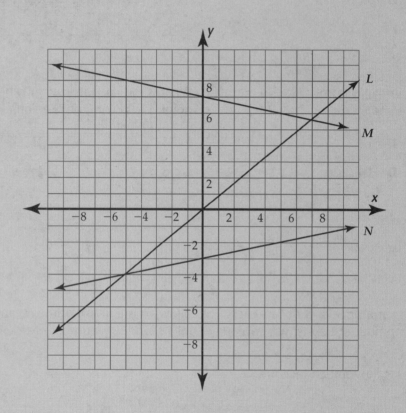

Step 1 At what point does line *L* intersect the *y*-axis? _____

Step 2 The *y*-intercept of line *L* is the *y*-coordinate of the point of intersection between line *L* and the *y*-axis. What is the *y*-intercept of line *L*? _____

Step 3 At what point does line *M* intersect the *y*-axis? _____

Step 4 What is the *y*-intercept of line *M*? _____

Step 5 At what point does line *N* intersect the *y*-axis? _____

Step 6 What is the *y*-intercept of line *N*? _____

Practice

Use the graph below to answer questions 1–6.

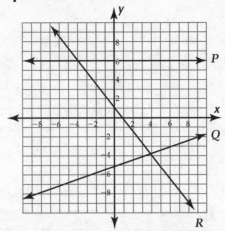

1 What are the coordinates of the point of intersection between the *y*-axis and line *P*?

A (0, 0)   **C** (0, 5)

B (0, 1)   **D** (0, 6)

2 What is the *y*-intercept of line *P*?

F 0   **H** 5

G 1   **J** 6

3 What is the point of intersection between the *y*-axis and line *Q*?

A (0, −5)   **C** (0, 1)

B (0, −2)   **D** (0, 3)

4 What is the *y*-intercept of line *Q*?

F −5   **H** 1

G −2   **J** 3

5 What is the *y*-intercept of line *R*?

A 5   **C** −3

B 1   **D** −6

6 What is the slope of line *P*?

F 0   **H** 5

G 1   **J** 6

Short-Response Question

7 A girl starts running straight down the street away from her house when she is 11 meters from home. She is running at a constant speed of 1 meter per second. The following is a graph of how far away she is from her house every second after she began running: *y* = distance from her house in meters, and *x* = how many seconds she has been running. What is the *y*-intercept of the graph? _____

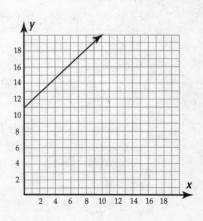

Think About It

A linear equation in one variable has a single solution, which can be represented as a point on a number line. For example, on a number line, the solution to the linear equation $x - 10 = 20$ is the single point $x = 30$.

A linear equation with two variables, such as $y = 2x - 3$, has infinitely many solutions and its graph is represented on a coordinate plane as a line. Given its equation, how can you use a table of values to create the graph of a line?

 Here's How

Use a table of values to graph the line whose equation is $y = 2x - 3$.

Step 1   Select several x-values. Then calculate the corresponding y-values.

Complete the table below.

x	$y = 2x - 3$	point on the line
-2	$y = 2(-2) - 3 = -4 - 3 = -7$	$(-2, -7)$
-1	$y = 2(-1) - 3 = -2 - 3 = -5$	$(-1, -5)$
0	$y = 2(0) - 3 = 0 - 3 = -3$	$(0, -3)$
1	$y = 2(1) - 3 = 2 - 3 = -1$	$(1, -1)$
2	$y = 2(2) - 3 = 4 - 3 = 1$	$(2, 1)$

Step 2   Plot the points from your table of values on the grid below.
Connect the points to draw the line that represents $y = 2x - 3$.

Be sure to extend your line in both directions beyond the points you have plotted. Include arrowheads at each end to show that the line continues.

Write the equation on the graph.

Step 3   Use your graph to find the y-coordinate of the point on the line that has $x = 5$.

Although only two points are required to draw a line, it is a good idea to use about five points when you have to create the graph of a line. Be sure to include some negative values.

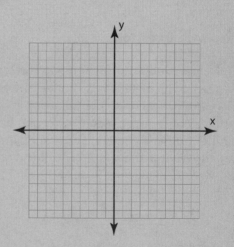

Notice that there are infinitely many points on the line, not only the points with integer coordinates. When selecting x-values, choose values that will avoid fractional values for y.

 **Practice**

Finish filling in the table of values for $y = -\frac{3}{2}x + 8$.

Table of Values for $y = -\frac{3}{2}x + 8$

x	$y = -\frac{3}{2}x + 8$	point on the line
-4	$y = -(\frac{3}{2})(-4) + 8 = 6 + 8 = 14$	$(-4, 14)$
-2	$y = -(\frac{3}{2})(-2) + 8 = 3 + 8 = 11$	$(-2, 11)$
0		
2	$y = -(\frac{3}{2})2 + 8 = -3 + 8 = 5$	$(2, 5)$
4		

1 Which of the following graphs represents the line $y = -\frac{3}{2}x + 8$?

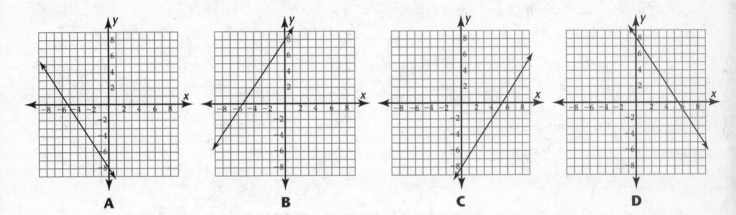

A   B   C   D

Short-Response Question

2 An extra large pizza with 20 slices is set out on a table at a party. Every minute, two slices of pizza are taken. This situation results in the linear equation $y = -2x + 20$ where y = number of slices of pizza that are left and x = minutes since the pizza was set on the table.

How many slices are there after 0 minutes? _____

How many minutes does it take for all of the pizza slices to be taken? _____

Graph the line.

Why should this line be graphed only for values between $x = 0$ and $x = 10$?

_____

_____

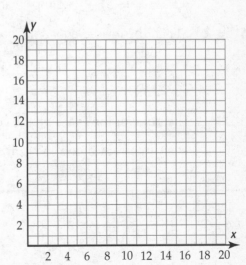

Performance indicators: **8.G.16, 8.CN.4**

> **READY REFERENCE**
>
> **slope-intercept form of a line** $y = mx + b$, where m represents the slope of the line and b represents the *y*-intercept

Think About It

How can you use the slope-intercept form of a line to write an equation for a line?
How can you use an equation for a line to find its slope and *y*-intercept?

Here's How

Write the equation of the line that has a slope of line 5 and a y-intercept of 11.

Step 1 Match the given values to letters in the general form $y = mx + b$.

The letter m, which represents the slope, will have the value _____.

The letter b, which represents the *y*-intercept, will have the value _____.

Step 2 Substitute for m and b in $y = mx + b$.

Using $m = 5$ and $b = 11$, an equation for the line is _____.

Determine the slope and y-intercept of the line whose equation is $2y = 3x - 10$.

Step 1 Put the given equation into the general form $y = mx + b$.

$2y = 3x - 10$ Divide each term of the equation by 2.

$\frac{2y}{2} = \frac{3x}{2} - \frac{10}{2}$

$y = \frac{3}{2x} + (-5)$ Simplify and put into the form of $y = mx + b$.

Step 2 Match the revised equation against $y = mx + b$.

$y = \frac{3}{2x} - 5$

$y = mx + b$

The slope of the line is m, the coefficient of *x*. The slope = _____

The *y*-intercept of the line is b, the constant term. The *y*-intercept is _____.

Measuring Up® to the New York State Learning Standards

Practice

Show your work.

1 What is the equation of a line with a slope equal to 2 and a y-intercept equal to 0?

A $y = 2$

B $y = x + 2$

C $y = 2x$

D $y = 2x + 2$

2 What is the equation of a line with a slope equal to $-\frac{3}{4}$ and a y-intercept equal to 7?

F $y = -\frac{3}{4}x + 7$

G $y = \frac{3}{4}x - 7$

H $y = 7x - \frac{3}{4}$

J $y = 7x + \frac{3}{4}$

3 What is the slope of the line whose equation is $y = 90x - 57$?

A -90

B -57

C 57

D 90

4 What is the y-intercept of the line whose equation is $y = 68x - 114$?

F -114

G -68

H 68

J 114

5 What is the slope of the line whose equation is $3y = 6x + 4$?

A 6

B $6x$

C 2

D $2x$

Short-Response Question

6 A tree is planted when it is 15 inches tall. It is growing at a constant rate of 6 inches a year. What equation of a line would represent the growth if y equals the number of inches tall the tree is and x equals the number of years that have passed since the tree was planted? _____

What is the slope of the line for this equation? _____

What is the y-intercept for this line? _____

Performance indicators: **8.G.17, 8.CN.2**

 Think About It

How can you graph an equation in the form $y = mx + b$?

 Here's How

Graph the line whose equation is $y = 4x + 2$.

Step 1 Check to be sure that the given equation is in the form $y = mx + b$.
Is $y = 4x + 2$ in the form $y = mx + b$? _____

Step 2 Determine the slope and the y-intercept from the given equation.
The slope of the line is _____.   The y-intercept of the line is _____.

Step 3 Plot the y-intercept on the graph below.
Mark a point at 2 on the y-axis.

Step 4 Use the slope to get more points for the line.
$4 <$ rise, go up 4

Write the slope as a ratio. $4 = \dfrac{4}{1}$ $\begin{array}{l}\leftarrow \text{rise, go up 4} \\ \leftarrow \text{run, go right 1}\end{array}$

Starting at the y-intercept, get another point by going up 4 and right 1.
Continue to get more points by following these instructions.

Step 5 Write an equivalent slope ratio using different signs.

Write the slope as a ratio. $4 = \dfrac{-4}{-1}$ $\begin{array}{l}\leftarrow \text{rise, go down 4} \\ \leftarrow \text{run, go left 1}\end{array}$

Go back to the y-intercept. Get another point by going down 4 and left 1.
Continue to get more points by following these instructions.

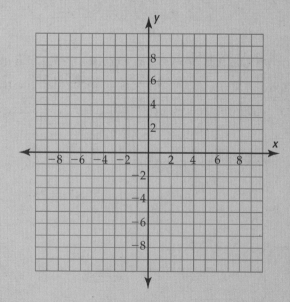

🔑 Practice

1 Given the equation for a line, $y = 3x - 3$, what are the coordinates of the *y*-intercept?

    A $(0, -3)$ **C** $(0, \frac{1}{3})$

    B $(0, -\frac{1}{3})$ **D** $(0, -3)$

2 What is the slope of this line?

    F -3 **H** 1

    G -1 **J** 3

3 Which is a way to get other points for this line?

    A Start at $(0, -3)$. Then go down 3 and right 1.   **C** Start at $(0, -3)$. Then go down 3 and up 1.

    B Start at $(0, -3)$. Then go up 3 and right 1.   **D** Start at $(0, -3)$. Then go down 3 and left 1.

4 Which of these graphs is a graph of the line?

F
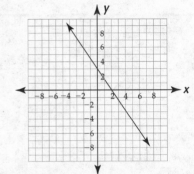

H
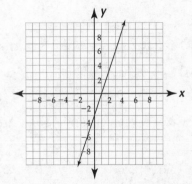

G
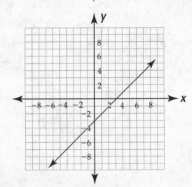

J
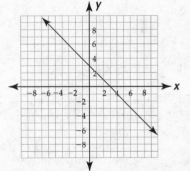

Short-Response Question

5 A boy enters a lighthouse. There are 5 steps below the door where he entered that lead to a basement room. However, the boy starts climbing up the stairs to the top of the lighthouse. He is climbing at a constant speed of 2 steps per second. This situation can be modeled by:

$y = 2x + 5$, where $y =$ the number of steps the boy is above the basement, and $x =$ the number of seconds that have passed since he began climbing the stairs.

Graph this line.

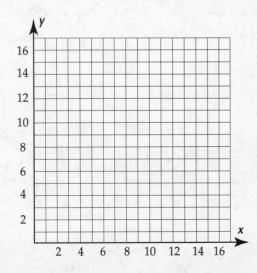

> **READY REFERENCE**
>
> **linear equation** an equation whose graph is a line
>
> **system of linear equations** two or more linear equations
>
> **solution set for a system of linear equations** the points on a graph that are common to all the lines of the system

 Think About It

How can you use a graph to find the solution set for a system of linear equations?

 Here's How

Find the solution set for this system of linear equations: $\left\langle \begin{array}{l} y = x + 2 \\ y = -2x + 8 \end{array} \right\rangle$

Step 1 Graph $y = x + 2$, the first line of the system, on the grid.

To use the slope-intercept method of graphing, plot the y-intercept at _____.

Then use the slope ratio $1 = \frac{1}{1} = \frac{-1}{-1}$ to get more points.

Step 2 Graph $y = -2x + 8$, the second line of the system, on the same grid.

Plot the y-intercept at 8.

Then use the slope ratio $-2 = \frac{-2}{1} = \frac{2}{-1}$ to get more points. Write the equation of each line near its graph.

Step 3 Write the coordinates of the point of intersection. The two lines intersect at the point _____, _____.

Step 4 Check that the point (2, 4) satisfies both equations.

$y = x + 2$ $y = -2x + 8$
$4 = 2 + 2$ $4 = -2(2) + 8$
$4 = 4$ $4 = -4 + 8$
                  $4 = 4$

Step 5 Write the solution set for the system.

$x =$ _____, $y =$ _____ also written as {(2, 4)}

🏷️ **Practice**

Show your work.

Look at the graph of the linear equations:

Line A: $y = x - 1$

Line B: $y = -x + 5$

Line C: $y = 3x + 1$

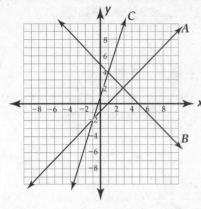

1 What is the solution set of the system containing the lines A and B?

    A (2, 3)   **C** $y = x - 1$

    B (3, 2)   **D** $y = -x + 5$

2 What is the solution set of the system containing the lines B and C?

    F (0, 1)   **H** (1, 4)

    G (0, 5)   **J** (2, 7)

3 What is the solution set of the system containing the lines A and C?

    A (−2, −1)   **C** (−1, 2)

    B (−1, −2)   **D** (2, −1)

4 What is the solution set of the system containing the lines A and $y = x - 1$?

    F $y = x - 1$ **H** $y = 3x + 1$

    G $y = -x + 5$ **J** (0, −1)

Short-Response Question

5 Graph the lines whose equations are $y = -x + 4$ and $y = 4x - 6$.

What is the solution set to this system of

equations? _____

Check that the solution satisfies both equations. Show all work.

For $y = -x + 4$,

$y = -2 + 4 =$ ____; (2, 2) is a point on the line.

For $y = 4x - 6$,

$y = 4 \cdot 2 - 6 =$ ____ ; (2, 2) is a point on the line.

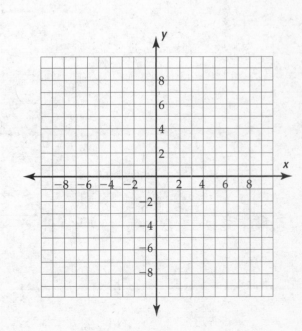

Think About It

Finding the solution set that satisfies an inequality is similar to finding the solution set that satisfies an equation. How can you find and graph the solution set for the following inequality?

$$-3x - 8 \leq 7$$

Here's How

Solve and graph an inequality on a number line.

Step 1 Consider the inequality $-3x - 8 \leq 7$.

Is $x = 0$ a solution to this inequality? _____

Step 2 Add 8 to both sides of the inequality to remove the -8 from the left side of the inequality.

$$-3x - 8 + 8 \leq 7 + 8$$

Simplify: $\qquad -3x + 0 \leq 15$

$$-3x \leq 15$$

Check: Is $x = 0$ a solution to this inequality? _____

Step 3 Divide both sides of the inequality by -3 to get rid of the -3 multiplied by x. Reverse the direction of the inequality because you are dividing the inequality by a negative number.

$$\frac{-3x}{-3} \geq \frac{15}{-3}$$

Simplify: $\qquad x \geq -5$

Check: Is $x = 0$ a solution to this inequality? _____

Step 4 Graph the solution set to this inequality on a number line.

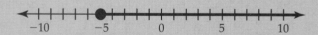

The closed circle indicates that -5 is included in the solution set.

Check: Is $x = 0$ part of the solution graphed on this number line? _____

Measuring Up® to the New York State Learning Standards

Practice

Show your work.

1 What is the solution set of the inequality
$4x + 9 < 11$?

   A $x < \frac{1}{2}$ **C** $x > \frac{1}{2}$

   B $x < 5$ **D** $x > 5$

2 What is the solution set of the inequality
$7x - 68 > 9$?

   F $x < -17$ **H** $x > -17$

   G $x < 11$ **J** $x > 11$

3 What is the solution set of the inequality
$-2x + 27 < 53$?

   A $x < -13$

   B $x < 13$

   C $x > -13$

   D $x > 13$

4 What is the solution set of the inequality
$-x + 15 \geq 18$?

   F (number line, closed dot at 3, -10 -5 0 5 10)

   G (number line, closed dot at -3, -10 -5 0 5 10)

   H (number line, closed dot at 3, -10 -5 0 5 10)

   J (number line, closed dot at -3, -10 -5 0 5 10)

5 What is the solution set of the inequality
$\frac{1}{2}x - 13 < -10$?

   A (number line, closed dot at -3, -10 -5 0 5 10)

   B (number line, open dot at 6, -10 -5 0 5 10)

   C (number line, open dot at 4, -10 -5 0 5 10)

   D (number line, open dot at 6, -10 -5 0 5 10)

Short-Response Question

6 Consider the inequality $-8x + 22 > 18 - 7x$.

Is $x = -10$ a solution of the inequality? _____
Is $x = 0$ a solution of the inequality? _____
Is $x = 10$ a solution of the inequality? _____

What is the solution of the inequality? _____

Graph the solution set of the inequality on the number line.

Performance indicators: **8.G.20, 8.R.2**

> **READY REFERENCE**
> **linear equation** an equation whose graph is a line; *example:* $y = 2x - 3$
> **nonlinear equation** an equation whose graph is not a line; *example:* $y = x^2$
> **ordered pair** a point in the coordinate plane where the first value corresponds
> to the x-value and the second to the $y =$ value; *example:* $(3, -2)$

Think About It

What do the graphs of the equations $y = -2 + 6$ and $y = x^2$ look like? How can you tell which of these equations is linear and which is nonlinear? When you plot the values in a table, you will begin to see a "picture" of each equation.

Another way to tell if an equation is linear is by studying the equation. Linear equations have one or two variables, each in the first power. So, $y = -2x + 6$ is _____. If either variable is raised to a power other than 0 or 1, or if the variables are multiplied by each other, the graph is not linear. For example, $y = x^2$ is _____.

Here's How

Inspect the Graph.

If you graph the equation and the graph is a straight line, it is a linear equation. If the graph is not a straight line, the equation is a nonlinear equation.

Step 1 Make tables for each equation.

$y = -2x + 6$

x	y
2	
	6
4	
	0

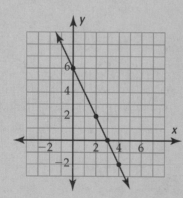

$y = x^2$

x	y
−2	
	1
0	
	1
2	

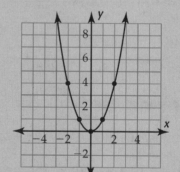

Step 2 Graph the points. Connect the points and label each equation.

Which graph is a line? _____

Which graph is nonlinear? _____

Step 3 Consider the equation $xy = 5$. Rewrite by multiplying both sides by x^{-1}. The equation becomes $y = 5x^{-1}$.

Is this equation linear or nonlinear? _____

Practice

1 Which equation is linear?

A $y = \frac{1}{2}x + 3$ **C** $x = y^3 + 3$

B $y = 2x^2 + 3$ **D** $y^2 = x + 3$

2 Which equation is nonlinear?

F $y = \frac{2}{5}x - 6$ **H** $y = 3x - 6$

G $x = \frac{2}{5}y - 6$ **J** $y = \frac{5}{2}x - 6$

3 Complete the table and graph the equation $2x + 2y = 8$.

x	y
	0
3	
1	3

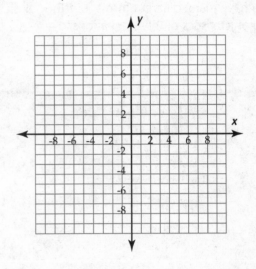

Is the equation linear or nonlinear? _____

Short-Response Question

4 Complete the table below for the equation $y = x^2 - 3$ where $x = -2, -1, 0, 1,$ and 2. Then plot the ordered pairs in the coordinate plane.

x	y
-2	1
-1	
1	
2	

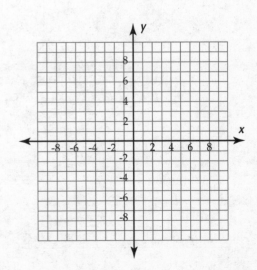

Is the equation linear or nonlinear? _____

> **READY REFERENCE**
>
> **quadratic equation** an equation in the form of $y = ax^2 + bx + c$, where $a \neq 0$ and a, b, and c are real numbers; *example:* $y = 2x^2 - 3x + 5$

 Think About It

A quadratic equation can have many different forms, but they all share some common characteristics. What are the common characteristics of these equations?

 Here's How

Form of a quadratic equation in one variable:

A quadratic equation can be written in one variable as
$$ax^2 + bx + c = 0 \quad \text{or} \quad ay^2 + by + c = 0.$$

Is each of the following a quadratic equation?

$y^2 - 4 = 0$ _____   The equation can be rewritten with $a =$ ___, $b =$ ___, and $c =$ ___.

$2x^3 = 2$ _____   The exponent of the variable must be 2.

$2x^2 = 2x$ _____   The equation can be rewritten with $a =$ ___, $b =$ ___, and $c =$ ___.

Symmetry of the y-values and the graph:

Look at the graph of $y = x^2 + 1$. For each point on the _____ side of the y-axis, there is a matching point on the _____ side.

In the table, you can also see symmetry in the y-values.

When $x = -3$ or 3, $y = 10$.
When $x = -2$ or 2, $y = 5$.

x	y
-3	10
-2	5
-1	2
0	1
1	2
2	5
3	10

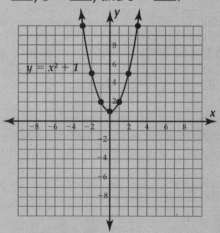

Shape of the graph:

A quadratic equation always has a minimum or a maximum value. When the equation contains x^2, the shape of the graph can be a "hill" or a "valley." When the equation contains y^2, the graph can "open" to the right or to the left.

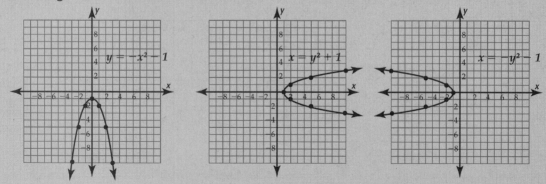

 Practice

Use the graphs below to answer questions 1–6.

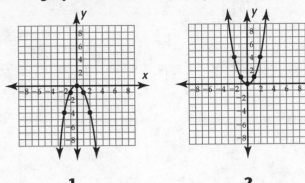
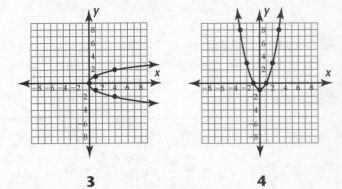

1   2   3   4

1   Develop a table of ordered pairs for the equation below. Then use the values in your table to determine which of the graphs shown above represents this equation.

$y = x^2$

x	y

A Graph 1   **B** Graph 3

B Graph 2   **D** Graph 4

2   Develop a table of ordered pairs for the equation below. Then use the values in your table to determine which of the graphs shown above represents this equation.

$y = x^2 - 1$

x	y

F Graph 1   **H** Graph 3

G Graph 2   **J** Graph 4

3   Develop a table of ordered pairs for the equation below. Then use the values in your table to determine which of the graphs shown above represents this equation.

$y = -x^2$

x	y

A Graph 1   **C** Graph 3

B Graph 2   **D** Graph 4

4   Develop a table of ordered pairs for the equation below. Then use the values in your table to determine which of the graphs shown above represents this equation.

$x = y^2$

x	y

F Graph 1   **H** Graph 3

G Graph 2   **J** Graph 4

5   Which graph has a minimum x-value of 0?

A Graph 1   **B** Graph 2   **C** Graph 3   **D** Graph 4

6   Which graph has a maximum y-value of 0?

F Graph 1   **G** Graph 2   **H** Graph 3   **J** Graph 4

Short-Response Question

7   A golf shot leaves the ground, travels in a curved path to a maximum height, and then falls in a curved path back to the ground. Could the flight of the golf ball be described by a quadratic equation? Explain your reasoning.

_____

_____

Think About It

How can you make a graph for an equation when the equation does not show y expressed in terms of x?

 Here's How

Graph the equation $2y + 2x - 10 = 0$.

Step 1 Is the equation linear or nonlinear? _____

Step 2 Decide on the method of graphing.
Choose the slope-intercept method.

Step 3 Put the equation in $y = mx + b$ form.

Solve the original equation for y in terms of x.

$2y + 2x - 10 = 0$	
$2y + 2x - 10 + 10 = 0 + 10$	Add 10 to each side.
$2y + 2x = 10$	Simplify.
$2y + 2x - 2x = 10 - 2x$	Subtract $2x$ from each side.
$2y = -2x + 10$	Simplify and rearrange.
$2y \div 2 = (-2x + 10) \div 2$	Divide each side by 2.
$y = $ _____	Simplify.

Step 4 Read the slope and y-intercept from the equation.

What is the slope of the line? _____
What is the y-intercept of the line? _____

Step 5 Use the slope and y-intercept to graph the line.

The y-intercept has been plotted for you at _____.

The slope can be written as $-1 = \frac{-1}{1}$.

To find the next point, move _____ 1 and right 1.
Repeat this procedure to find more points.
Draw the line and label it.

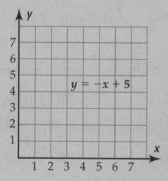

Practice

Show your work.

1 What is the slope-intercept form of the line whose equation is $3y + 9x = 24$?

A $y = 3x + 8$ **C** $y = -2x + 6$

B $y = 2x + 6$ **D** $y = -3x + 8$

2 What is the slope-intercept form of the line whose equation is $2y - 4x = y - 9x + 11$?

F $y = -5x + 11$ **H** $y = -13x + 11$

G $y = 13x + 11$ **J** $y = 5x + 11$

3 For which equation must you use a table of values to graph?

A $y = x$ **C** $y - 2x = 0$

B $y = x^2 + 2$ **D** $y - 2x + 2 = 0$

4 Which of the following equations can be simpified by putting it into slope-intercept form?

F $y = x^2 + 4$ **H** $y + 2x = 3x$

G $y + y^2 = 4$ **J** $2y^2 = 2x^2$

Short-Response Question

5 A farmer takes a full basket that contains both apples and oranges to market every day. If he puts more oranges in the basket, there will be less room for the apples. If he puts more apples in the basket, there will be less room for the oranges.

The farmer discovered that the full basket can hold twenty less than twice the sum of the apples and oranges.

Let y = the number of apples the basket holds, and let x = the number of oranges the basket holds.

The basket holds $(y + x)$ apples and oranges. The farmer found this amount to be the same as $2(y + x) - 20$ apples and oranges.

This situation can be modeled by the equation $y + x = 2(y + x) - 20$.

Is this equation linear or nonlinear? _____

Rewrite the equation to write y in terms of x. _____

Graph the equation.

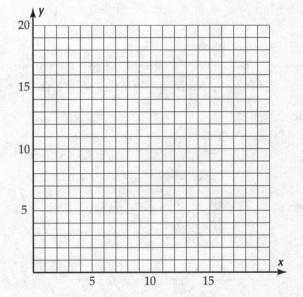

Performance indicators: **8.RP.2, 8.RP.4, 8.G.3**

> **READY REFERENCE**
>
> **exterior angle** the angle formed by one side of a polygon and the extension of the adjacent side
>
> **interior angle** the angle formed by two adjacent sides of a polygon; the sum of the measures of the interior angles in a triangle is 180° and in general is the sum $(n - 2)180°$, where n is the number of sides of the polygon

Think About It

Suppose you want to find the measure of the exterior angle of a regular hexagon. The formula for the sum of the measures of the interior angles of a polygon is

$$\text{sum of measures of interior angles} = (n - 2) \bullet 180$$

where n is the number of sides of the polygon. How can you use this formula to establish a new formula for the measure of the exterior angle?

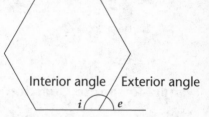

Interior angle / Exterior angle

Here's How

Use a familiar formula to establish another formula.

Step 1 Use the diagram to relate the measure of an interior angle i to the measure of the exterior angle e.

The angles are supplementary, so the measures of $\angle e$ and $\angle i$ add to _____.

Therefore, $m\angle e = 180 - m\angle i$.

Step 2 Use the known formula to find the measure of the interior angle e.

$$\text{sum of measures of interior angles} = (n - 2) \bullet 180$$

Because the polygon is regular, each interior angle is equal. Therefore, for a regular polygon with n sides, the formula becomes

$$\text{sum of measures of interior angles} \div n = (n - 2) \bullet 180 \div n$$

Divide both sides by n.

$m\angle i = \left(\frac{n-2}{n}\right) \bullet 180$	Rearrange.
$m\angle i = \left(\frac{n}{n} - \frac{2}{n}\right) \bullet 180$	Use the Distributive Property.
$m\angle i = \left(1 - \frac{2}{n}\right) \bullet 180$	Simplify.
$m\angle i = 180 - \frac{360}{n}$	Use the Distributive Property.

Step 3 Substitute into the formula for $m\angle e$.

$m\angle e = 180 - m\angle i$	Substitute in $m\angle i = 180 - \frac{360}{n}$.
$m\angle e = 180 - \left(180 - \frac{360}{n}\right)$	Distribute the negative sign.
$m\angle e = \frac{360}{n}$	Simplify.

Conclusion: For any regular n-gon, the measure of an exterior angle is _____.

Practice

Use the formulas in the diagram on the right to answer questions 1–2.

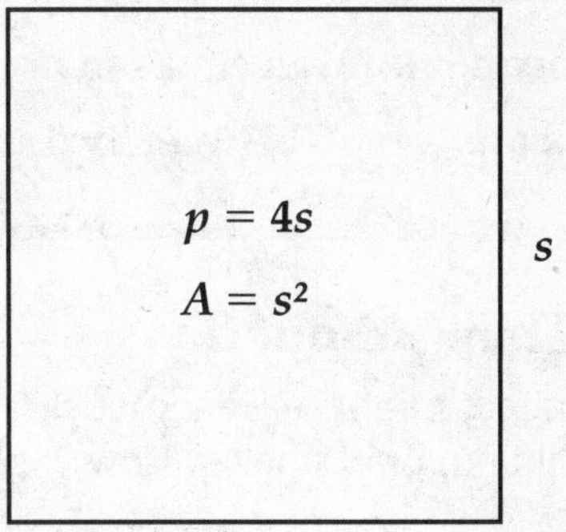

1 Given the formulas for the perimeter and area of a square, what is the formula for the area of a square in terms of the perimeter?

A $A = 4s^2$

C $A = \frac{s}{16}$

B $A = \frac{p^2}{16}$

D $A = 16p^2$

$$p = 4s$$
$$A = s^2$$
s

2 Which of the following formulas gives the perimeter of a square in terms of the area?

F $p = 4A$

H $p = 16A$

G $p = 4\sqrt{A}$

J $p = 16\sqrt{A}$

Use the formulas in the diagram on the right to answer questions 3–4.

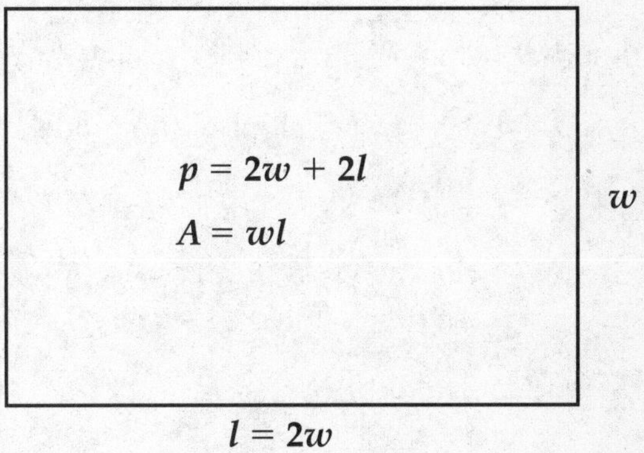

3 The general formula for the perimeter of a rectangle is $p = 2w + 2l$. For this particular rectangle, the length l is twice the width w. What is the formula for the perimeter of this particular rectangle?

A $p = 2w$

C $p = 6w$

B $p = 4w$

D $p = 8w$

$$p = 2w + 2l$$
$$A = wl$$
w

$l = 2w$

4 The general formula for the area of a rectangle is $A = wl$. What is the formula for the area of this particular rectangle?

F $A = 2w$

G $A = 2w^2$

H $A = 4w$

J $A = 4w^2$

Short-Response Question

5 You are given the formulas for the perimeter and area of a square in terms of the length of a side:

$$p = 4s$$

$$A = s^2$$

Is the numerical value of the area A *always* greater than the numerical value of the perimeter p? Support your conclusion.

_____

_____

_____

_____

Performance indicators: **8.CM.10, 8.PS.10, 8.CN.8, 8.R.9**

READY REFERENCE

proportion an equation in the form $\frac{a}{b} = \frac{c}{d}$ showing that two ratios are equal

scale a ratio between two sets of measurements

 Think About It

An architect might make a model of a building she is planning. She makes the model look exactly like the real building, only smaller. How can she be sure her model has the same proportions as the building?

 Here's How

Use scale models.

A scale model shows the proportions of an object, but not the actual size. Given a scale of 1 in. : $2\frac{1}{2}$ ft, find the height of a model if the actual height is 75 ft.

Step 1 Let h = the height of the model.

$$\frac{\text{scale}}{\text{actual}} = \frac{1 \text{ in.}}{2.5 \text{ ft}} = \frac{h}{75 \text{ ft}}$$

Step 2 Write the cross products.

$2.5h = 75$ in.

Step 3 Solve for h.

$h =$ _____ in.

What is the height of the model? _____ in.

Find unknown lengths.

Given that trapezoid *ABCD* is similar to trapezoid *WXYZ*, find *m*.

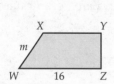 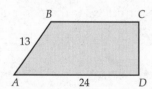

Step 1 Set up proportions.

$\frac{AD}{WZ} = \frac{AB}{WX}$

Step 2 Substitute the lengths.

$\frac{24}{16} = \frac{13}{m}$

Step 3 Write the cross products and solve for *m*. Round to the nearest tenth.

$24m =$ _____

$m =$ _____

🔑 Practice

1 Given that the parallelograms are similar, find each unknown length.

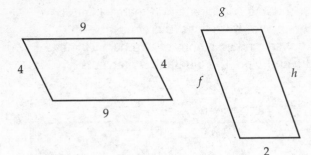

A $f = 18$, $g = 2$, $h = 18$

B $f = 18$, $g = 4$, $h = 4.5$

C $f = 4.5$, $g = 4$, $h = 4.5$

D $f = 4.5$, $g = 2$, $h = 4.5$

2 Tamara and her grandfather are making a picnic table that is proportional to her parents' larger picnic table. What is the length of side y?

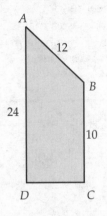
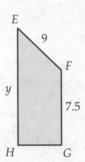

F $y = \frac{3}{4}$ **H** $y = 18$

G $y = 9$ **J** $y = 32$

3 The scale on a map is 1 in. : 20 mi. What is the actual distance between two cities that are $2\frac{3}{4}$ in. apart on a map?

A 35 mi   **C** 55 mi

B 45 mi   **D** 65 mi

4 A computer screen is 10 in. wide and 14 in. long. A movie screen is a similar rectangle with a width of 20 ft. What is the length of the movie screen?

F 140 ft   **H** 28 ft

G 30 ft   **J** 24 ft

5 Kent wants to make a scale drawing of a dinosaur that is 46 ft tall and 73 ft long on a sheet of paper that is $8\frac{1}{2}$ in. by 11 in. Which of the following scales could he use?

A 1 in. = 8 ft   **C** 1 in. = 4 ft

B 1 in. = 5 ft   **D** 1 in. = 2 ft

6 Lauren is writing a report on band instruments. She wants to sketch a trumpet for her report. The actual trumpet is about 6 in. wide and 21 in. long. At a scale of 1 in. : 3 in., what would be the length of the trumpet in her sketch?

F 2 in.   **H** 63 in.

G 18 in.   **J** 7 in.

Short-Response Question

7 The scale for a drawing shown on graph paper indicates that 1 square is equal to 2 ft. How many squares on the paper would be shaded to show the length of a room that is 25 ft on a side?

_____

_____

_____

_____

Performance indicators: **8.CN.2, 8.G.10, 8.G.13**

🔑 Think About It

Parallel lines are the same fixed distance apart and never intersect. On a coordinate grid, parallel lines have the same slope. This occurs because for every equivalent change in x for both lines, there must be an equivalent change in y for both lines to maintain their fixed distance. The equations of two parallel lines will be $y = mx + a$ and $y = mx + b$, where m is the slope and a and b are the different y-intercepts.

🔑 Here's How

Determine whether two lines are parallel.

Step 1   Look at the graph of the lines $y = x$ and $y = x + 5$.

Step 2   What point is on the line $y = x$ when $x = 0$? _____

        What point is on the line $y = x + 5$ when $x = 0$?

        _____

Step 3   What is the difference between $y = x + 5$ and $y = x$ when $x = 0$? ____

Step 4   What is the difference in y-values between the lines $y = x + 5$ and $y = x$ at every value of x?

        $y_1 = x + 5$ and $y_2 = x$

        $y_1 - y_2 = (x + 5) - x =$ _____

Step 5   This means that $y = x + 5$ and $y = x$ are a fixed distance apart.

        Are $y = x + 5$ and $y = x$ parallel? _____

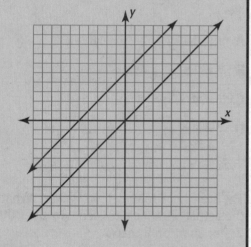

Show that a vertical translation creates a parallel line.

Step 1   Consider the graph of the line $y = 2x + 1$. Then vertically translate this graph $+ 3$ units.

Step 2   A vertical translation moves an entire graph up or down by a specific amount. In this case, it was three units. Are these two lines parallel lines? _____

Step 3   What is the slope of the new line? _____

Step 4   What is the y-intercept of the new line? _____

Step 5   What is the equation of the new line? _____

Step 6   Is this equation the same as adding three to every y-value of the original equation? _____

        Start with $y = 2x + 1$ and add 3.

        $y = 2x + 1 + 3 =$ _____

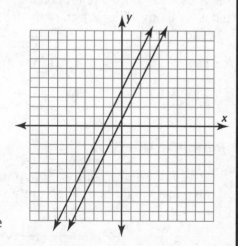

 **Practice**

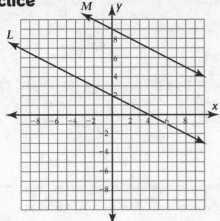

1 Look at the graph at the left. What vertical translation occurred from line L to line M?

A $+2$

B $+5$

C $+7$

D $+9$

2 Which line is parallel to the line $y = -11x + 32$?

F $y = -11x + 8$ **H** $y = 11x + 1$

G $y = x + 32$ **J** $y = 32x - 11$

3 What is the fixed vertical distance between corresponding points on the lines $y = 102x + 20$ and $y = 102x - 30$?

A 20   **C** 50

B 30   **D** 60

4 Consider the line $y = 5x + 16$. If you vertically translate the graph of this line by moving it down nine units, what is the equation of the transformed line?

F $y = 5x + 9$ **H** $y = 5x + 5$

G $y = 5x + 7$ **J** $y = 5x + 3$

5 Which equation of a line has a graph that is a vertical translation of $y = -6x - 1$ by a fixed distance of 12 units?

A $y = -6x - 13$ **C** $y = 6x - 12$

B $y = -6x + 12$ **D** $y = 6x + 13$

Short-Response Question

6 Two buildings are being built up floor by floor at the same rate of one floor per week. The second building began construction when the first building had just completed its eighth floor. Given that y equals the number of floors built and x equals the number of weeks that have past since the second building began construction, the equation for the second building's construction is $y = x$.

What is the equation of the first building's construction given the same variables x and y?

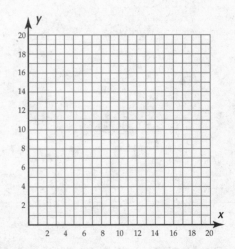

_____

Graph the two lines representing the construction of each building.

Is the line of the first building's construction a vertical translation of the line of the second building's construction? _____

If so, what is the distance of the vertical translation? _____

Lesson 58 **Focus on Representation: Use Representation
to Explore Mathematical Ideas**

Performance indicators: **8.R.8, 8.G.13**

Think About It

The slope of a line is the rise divided by the run, or the vertical change divided by the horizontal change.
There are many different ways to represent this constant rate. One way to represent slope is as the ratio of
the horizontal leg to the vertical leg of a right triangle formed by using the line for the hypotenuse.

Here's How

Create similar right triangles using the graph of a line to form their hypotenuses.

Step 1   Look at the graph of the line $y = 2x$ and the two right
triangles with hypotenuses attached to the line, triangles
A and B.

Step 2   What are the lengths of the legs of Triangle A? _____

What are the lengths of the legs of Triangle B? _____

Step 3   Are Triangle A and Triangle B similar? _____

Step 4   What is the ratio of the length of Triangle A's horizontal

leg to the length of its vertical leg? _____

What is the ratio of the length of Triangle B's horizontal

leg to the length of its vertical leg? _____

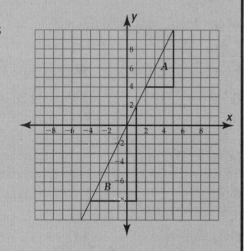

Step 5   If Triangle A and Triangle B are similar, their corresponding sides are proportional. This means
that the ratio of their horizontal legs is equal to the ratio of their vertical legs: $\frac{3}{5} = \frac{6}{10}$.
Is this true? _____

Step 6   Since these two ratios are equal, it is also true that the ratio of the lengths of one triangle's
vertical and horizontal legs is equal to the ratio of the lengths of the other triangle's vertical
and horizontal legs.

$\frac{3}{5} = \frac{6}{10}$ $3(\frac{10}{5})/3 =$ _____

$10(\frac{3}{5}) = 10(\frac{6}{10})$

$3(\frac{10}{5}) = 6$ $\frac{10}{5} =$ _____

These are the equal ratios of the lengths of the triangles' vertical legs to their horizontal legs.
Do these ratios equal the slope? _____

Using right triangles to find negative slopes.

Step 1   Look at the graph of the right triangle on the next page.

What is the ratio of the length of this triangle's vertical leg to the length of its horizontal leg? ____

Step 2   Can the ratio of the lengths of a triangle's legs ever be negative? _____

Step 3 A line that decreases as its *x*-values increase has a negative slope, and a line that increases as its *x*-values increase has a positive slope. Does the line that runs through the hypotenuse of this triangle have a positive or a negative slope? _____

Step 4 What does the slope of the line that runs through the

hypotenuse of this triangle equal? _____

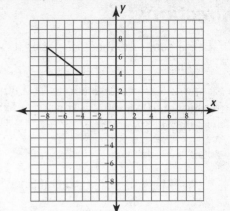

Practice

Use the figure at right to answer questions 1–3.

 1 What is the slope of the line that runs through the hypotenuse of triangle *C*?

A −1   **C** 1

B $-\frac{6}{7}$ **D** $\frac{6}{7}$

2 What is the slope of the line that runs through the hypotenuse of triangle *D*?

F $\frac{8}{3}$ **H** $-\frac{3}{8}$

G $\frac{3}{8}$ **J** $-\frac{8}{3}$

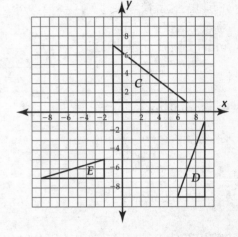

3 What is the slope of the line that runs through the hypotenuse of triangle *E*?

A $-\frac{7}{2}$ **C** $\frac{2}{7}$

B $-\frac{2}{7}$ **D** $\frac{7}{2}$

4 A right triangle has its hypotenuse along the line $y = (\frac{2}{3})x - 4$. The length of its horizontal leg is 9. What is the length of its vertical leg?

F 2   **H** 4

G 3   **J** 6

5 If you draw a right triangle with its hypotenuse along the line $y = -5x + 11$ and with the length of its vertical leg equal to 15, what is the length of its horizontal leg?

A $\frac{1}{5}$ **B** $\frac{1}{3}$ **C** 3   **D** 5

Short-Response Question

6 A tall pole creates a shadow on the ground. The slope of the line formed between the top of the pole and the top of the shadow is $-\frac{5}{2}$. Sketch the line on the grid.

If the length of the shadow is 12 ft, how tall is the pole? _____

Later on in the day, the shadow grows longer and the slope of the new line formed between the top of the pole and the top of the shadow is $-\frac{2}{3}$. Sketch the line on the grid. How long is the shadow? _____

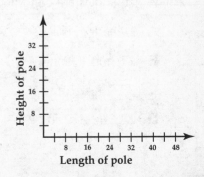

Directions

Use a separate sheet of paper to show your work.

1 ∠A and ∠B are vertical angles. If ∠B has a measure of 104°, what is the sum of the measures of ∠A and ∠B?

A 52°   **C** 180°

B 90°   **D** 208°

2 Look at the figure.

If sides *a* and *b* are two sides of a rectangle, what type of angles are angle *C* and angle *D*?

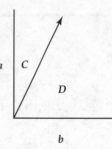

F complementary angles

G supplementary angles

H obtuse angles

J vertical angles

For questions 3–6, use the figure of two pairs of intersecting parallel lines.

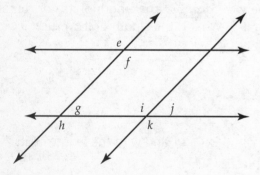

3 Which angles are congruent to ∠e?

A ∠f and ∠i only

B ∠g and ∠k only

C ∠f, ∠h, ∠i, and ∠k

D ∠i, ∠k, ∠g, and ∠j

4 What is the sum of the measures of ∠g, ∠h, ∠i, and ∠j ?

F 90°   **H** 270°

G 180°   **J** 360°

5 Given that the measure of ∠g is 52°, what is the measure of ∠i ?

A 38°   **C** 116°

B 52°   **D** 128°

6 Given that the measure of ∠g is 52°, what is the measure of ∠e?

F 38°   **H** 116°

G 52°   **J** 128°

7 Consider △R graphed on the coordinate grid.

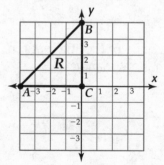

Triangle *R* is reflected across the *x*-axis. What will be the coordinates of B′?

A (0, −4)

B (0, 0)

C (4, 0)

D (−4, 0)

8 Look at the graph of the line $y = x$.

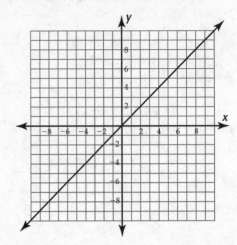

Which linear equation's graph is a translation of the line $y = x$?

F $y = -2x + 3$ **H** $y = 5x - 5$

G $y = x + 7$ **J** $y = 8x$

9 A triangle is transformed into a similar triangle and with the same orientation as the original triangle. What is this type of transformation?

A dilation   **C** rotation

B reflection   **D** translation

10 Suppose you reflect the rectangle across the dashed line.

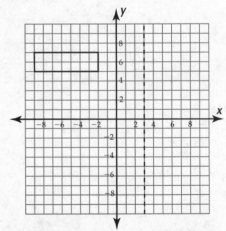

What does the point $(-2, 6)$ in the original rectangle become when it is reflected?

F $(2, 6)$ **H** $(5, 6)$

G $(3, 6)$ **J** $(8, 6)$

For questions 11–12, refer to the following graph.

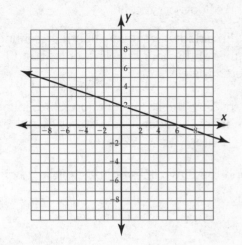

11 What is the slope of the line?

A 3   **C** $-\frac{1}{3}$

B $\frac{1}{3}$ **D** -3

12 What is the y-intercept of the line?

F 2   **H** -2

G 0   **J** 7

13 What is the point on the line $y = \frac{5}{4}x + 9$, where $x = 8$?

A $(8, 14)$ **C** $(8, 27)$

B $(8, 19)$ **D** $(8, 29)$

14 What is the equation of a line with a slope equal to 11 and a y-intercept equal to -2?

F $y = 11x - 2$ **H** $y = (\frac{1}{11})x - 2$

G $y = -2x + 11$ **J** $y = -(\frac{1}{2})x + 11$

15   A boy and a girl are in a tall office building. They each enter different elevators at the same time. The girl enters on the sixth floor, and the boy enters on the twentieth floor. The girl's elevator rises at a constant speed of a half floor per second, and the boy's elevator descends at a constant speed of three floors per second.

For the girl, the linear equation representing this situation is $y = \frac{1}{2}x + 6$, where y equals the number of the floor her elevator is at and x equals the seconds that have passed since she entered the elevator.

For the boy, the linear equation representing this situation is $y = -3x + 20$, where y equals the number of the floor his elevator is at and x equals the seconds that have passed since he entered the elevator.

Graph these two lines on the coordinate grid.

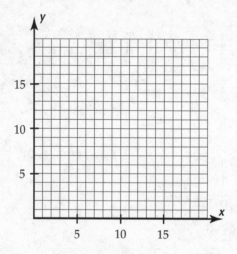

After how many seconds will the boy and girl pass the same floor? _____

At which floor will they pass each other? _____

16 Complete the table of values for each equation. Show your work.

Table of Values for $y = x^2 + x + 5$

x	$y = x^2 + x + 5$	point on the graph
0		
1		
2		
3		

Table of Values for $y = 4x + 5$

x	$y = 4x + 5$	point on the graph
0		
1		
2		
3		

The equation $y = x^2 + x + 5$ is a _____ equation.

The equation $y = 4x + 5$ is a _____ equation.

What are two points of intersection between the quadratic and the line? _____.

READY REFERENCE

Fahrenheit a scale for measuring temperature; on the Fahrenheit scale, water boils at 212°F and freezes at 32°F

Celsius a scale for measuring temperature; on the Celsius scale, water boils at 100°C and freezes at 0°C

Customary Units of Length

1 foot (ft) = 12 inches (in.)   1 yard (yd) = 36 inches
1 yard = 3 feet   1 mile (mi) = 5,280 feet or 1,760 yards

Metric Units of Length

1 centimeter (cm) = 10 millimeters (mm)   1 decimeter (dm) = 10 centimeters
1 meter (m) = 100 centimeters   1 kilometer (km) = 1,000 meters

---

Think About It

Communication satellites can orbit Earth at about 11,000 miles above the surface. How many feet above the Earth's surface are the satellites? Sydney, Australia, the site of the 2000 summer Olympics, is about 14,862,000 meters from Chicago. How many kilometers apart are the two cities? The average body temperature of a human is 98.6°F. What is this temperature in degrees Celsius?

Here's How

To convert customary units of length, use a ratio.

1. Use the ratio $\frac{5,280 \text{ ft}}{1 \text{ mi}}$.

2. $\frac{11,000 \text{ mi}}{1} \cdot \frac{5,280 \text{ ft}}{1 \text{ mi}} = \frac{11,000 \cdot 5,280}{1}$ ft $= 58,080,000$ ft

3. The satellites are about _____ million ft above Earth's surface.

Hint: When converting larger units to smaller units, use the ratio with the number of smaller units on top.

To convert metric units of length, use a ratio.

1. Use the ratio $\frac{1 \text{ km}}{1,000 \text{ m}}$.

2. $\frac{14,862,000 \text{ m}}{1} \cdot \frac{1 \text{ km}}{1,000 \text{ m}} = \frac{14,862,000 \text{ m} \cdot 1 \text{ km}}{1,000 \text{ m}} = \frac{14,862,000 \text{ km}}{1,000} = 14,862$ km

3. The two cities are about _____ kilometers apart.

Hint: When converting smaller units to larger units, use the ratio with the number of larger units on top.

Temperature conversions

1. Convert 98.6° Fahrenheit to Celsius. Use the formula $C = \frac{5}{9}(F - 32)$.

   $C = \frac{5}{9}(98.6 - 32)$, $C = \frac{5}{9}(66.6)$, $C = \frac{333}{9}$, $C =$ _____   So 98.6° F = _____ C.

2. To convert degrees Celsius to degrees Fahrenheit, use the formula $F = \frac{9}{5}C + 32$.

Practice

1 Mount Everest is the highest point in the world at 29,028 ft. What is its elevation in miles? Round to the nearest tenth.

A 87,084 mi

C 5.6 mi

B 9,676 mi

D 5.5 mi

2 The Grand Canyon is 277 miles long What is its length in inches?

F 17,550,720 in.

H 39,888 in.

G 1,462,560 in.

J 9,972 in.

3 What is the length of the Grand Canyon in yards?

A 831 yd

C 487,520 yd

B 3,324 yd

D 4,782,500 yd

4 A giant sequoia in Sequoia National Park, California, is 275 ft tall. What is its height in inches?

F 22.92 in.

H 6,600 in.

G 3,300 in.

J 9,900 in.

5 Convert 6° Celsius to degrees Fahrenheit.

A 48.2°F

C 32.2°F

B 42.8°F

D 21.11°F

6 Convert 84° Fahrenheit to degrees Celsius. Round to the nearest hundredth.

F 28.89°C

H 101.89°C

G 49.56°C

J 183.2°C

7 Convert 160° Celsius to degrees Fahrenheit.

A 71.12°F

C 230°F

B 113.34°F

D 320°F

8 Convert 116° Fahrenheit to degrees Celsius. Round to the nearest hundredth.

F 29.92°C

H 101.89°C

G 46.67°C

J 240.8°C

Short-Response Question

9 How many degrees colder would the weather be at 0°C than at 0°F? Show your work, and explain each step. Round to the nearest hundredth.

_____

_____

_____

_____

_____

> **READY REFERENCE**
>
> **proportion** an equation in the form $\frac{a}{b} = \frac{c}{d}$ showing that two ratios are equal
>
> **rate** a ratio comparing two different types of quantities, such as miles
> to hours or feet to seconds

 Think About It

The Nevilles are on a 400-mile trip to Buffalo, New York. They have driven 220 miles in 4 hours. If they continue traveling at this rate, how much time will the entire trip take?

Here's How

Use a proportion. Let t stand for the time the entire trip will take.

Step 1 Write a proportion comparing the miles they have traveled to the time they have traveled.

$$\frac{220}{4} = \frac{400}{t}$$

Step 2 Use cross products to solve for t.

$$\frac{220}{4} = \frac{400}{t}$$

$$220t = 1,600$$

$$t = \underline{\hspace{2cm}}$$

The entire trip will take _____ hours.

Practice

Show your work.

1   Don drives 45 miles in 1.5 hours. At this rate, how far could he drive in 7 hours? _____

2   Marsha rode her bike 4 miles in 0.5 hour. At this rate, how far did she ride in 3 hours? _____

3   Abdul drives 248 miles in 4 hours, and Jean drives 392 miles in 7 hours. Use cross products to determine whether these rates are equal.

4 If Kate travels 120 miles in 2 hours, how many miles per hour is she traveling?

A 240 mph   **C** 60 mph

B 180 mph   **D** 40 mph

5 A bottle-nosed dolphin can travel about 2.25 miles in 5 minutes. How many miles per hour can it travel?

F 11.25 mph   **H** 43 mph

G 27 mph   **J** 135 mph

6 The cheetah, the fastest land animal, has been clocked at a speed of 71 miles per hour. How many feet per hour is this?

A 369,200 ft   **C** 391,765 ft

B 374,880 ft   **D** 399,979 ft

7 What is the speed of a cheetah in feet per minute?

F 6,677 ft per minute

G 6,529 ft per minute

H 6,248 ft per minute

J 5,798 ft per minute

8 Kent has determined that he must ride his exercise bike 24 minutes at 13 miles per hour to burn off the calories from a 12-ounce can of soda. How long would he have to ride the bike at the same speed to burn off the calories from a 16-ounce bottle of soda?

A 30 minutes   **C** 48 minutes

B 32 minutes   **D** 96 minutes

9 The temperature increases 0.2°F per minute. How long will it be before the temperature increases 10°?

F 50 minutes

G 45 minutes

H 40 minutes

J 35 minutes

10 After takeoff, a jet ascends at 900 feet per minute. What altitude will it reach in $\frac{1}{3}$ hour?

A 36,000 ft   **C** 27,000 ft

B 30,000 ft   **D** 18,000 ft

11 It takes Elizabeth 8 hours to make one Navajo rope necklace from turquoise beads. How many necklaces will she make if she works 40 hours this week?

F 5   **H** 3.64

G 4.5   **J** 3

Short-Response Question

12 Emilio leaves New York on a cross-country car trip at 7:00 A.M. He averages 40 miles per hour. Ann plans to take exactly the same route but does not leave until 8:00 A.M. She averages 50 miles per hour. Draw a diagram or table to determine at what time Anne will catch up with Emilio. Write the answer on the line.

Think About It

When you use several steps to solve a problem, you need to be able to explain those steps.

 Here's How

Work with distances.

Claudia and Lisa, while driving in their jeep, notice that the exits on the highway are about 3 miles apart. They just passed Exit 113. They need to get off at Exit 85. Lisa predicts they have 90 more miles to travel. Do you agree or disagree? Explain.

Step 1 Use an organized procedure to find the number of exits to go.
How many more exits are there before Exit 85?

Subtract $113 - 85 =$ _____

Round the number of exits to the nearest 10. There are about _____ more exits to Exit 85.

Step 2 Convert from number of exits to number of miles.
The exits are about 3 miles apart. Calculate the number of miles to Exit 85.

30 exits $\times$ _____ between exits = _____ more miles

They will drive approximately _____ more miles to reach Exit 85.

Step 3 Compare the results to Lisa's prediction.
90 mi = _____ Lisa is correct.

Work with temperatures.

During one week in February, the daily low temperatures in Schenectady were 8°F, −3°F, −2°F, 1°F, 0°F, 2°F, and 1°F. Joaquin said that the average low temperature in Schenectady for that week was 17°C. Do you agree or disagree. Explain.

Step 1 Use an organized procedure to find the average low temperature in °F.

Add the positive integers. $8 + 1 + 2 + 1 =$ _____

Add the negative integers.   _____ + _____ = _____

Combine the sums.   _____ + _____ = _____

Divide the sum by the numbers of days in a week. $7 \div$ _____ = _____

Step 2 Convert from °F to °C. Round to the nearest whole.

$$T_{celsius} = \frac{5}{9}(T_{Fahrenheit} - 32) \qquad\qquad T_{celsius} = \frac{5}{9}(- \underline{\hspace{1cm}})$$

$$T_{celsius} = \frac{5}{9}(1 - 32) \qquad\qquad\qquad T_{celsius} = \underline{\hspace{1cm}}.$$

Step 3 Compare the results to Joaquin's. 17°C = _____.

Practice

For questions 1–4, write "yes" if you agree with the answer. If not, write the correct answer down.

1 Mrs. Cunningham recorded the height of each of her students in centimeters. Their heights were 160 cm, 172 cm, 155 cm, 165 cm, and 148 cm. Jim says that the average height of the students is 2 m. Is he right?

_____

_____

2 In a diving maneuver, a submarine began at a depth of −80 ft, then dived 200 ft. It then rose 150 ft. Capt. Nick says the depth of the submarine after this maneuver was $-43\frac{1}{3}$ yards. Is he right?

_____

_____

3 A plane flew to Pittsburgh at an altitude of 5,700 ft. As it came closer to Pittsburgh, the tower instructed the pilot to descend to 2,400 ft and hold that altitude. The pilot says the plane descended 1,107 yards to reach 2,400 ft. Is she right?

_____

_____

4 Geoff is 6 km from his house. He rides at a speed of $5.7\frac{km}{h}$. He says he will be 30 cm from his house in 1 hour. Is he right?

_____

_____

Extended-Response Question

5 The map below gives the distance in miles between each point.

Part A What are the 3 most direct routes from point *A* to point *F* ?

Route 1: _____

Route 2: _____

Route 3: _____

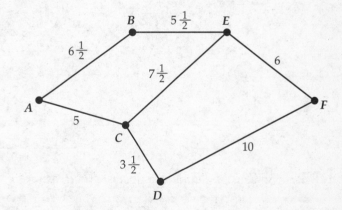

Part B How many miles is the shortest route from point *A* to point *F* ? _____

Explain the steps of your solution.

_____

_____

Performance indicators: **8.CM.4, 8.CM.2, 8.M.1**

Think About It

Mr. Kendall presented this problem to the class:

David and Matt live on the same road 4 miles apart. The Country Store is exactly halfway between them. Both boys begin riding their bikes at the same time and at the same rate of speed to meet each other. Halfway to the store, Matt realizes that he forgot his money at home. He goes back home, gets his money, and rides toward the store again. How far are Matt and David from the store when they finally meet?

Laura used a diagram to solve the problem. How can Laura share her conclusion with the class?

Here's How

Draw a Diagram

Step 1   Interpret Laura's diagram. In her diagram, Laura used A, B, C, to model the boys' movements.

Let A = the distance each rides halfway to the store.

Let B = the distance that Matt returns and the distance that David continues to ride toward Matt.

Let C = the distance that Matt travels back toward David, and the distance David continues to ride toward Matt.

Fill in the mileages in Laura's diagram.

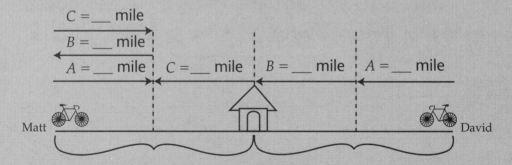

Step 2   Use Laura's diagram to answer the question.

How far are the boys from the store when they meet? _____

Step 3   Explain how to use Laura's digram to draw other conclusions.

Laura said that her diagram can be used to conclude the distance the boys are from Matt's house when they meet. What is another conclusion you can draw from Laura's diagram?

_____

Practice

Use a picture, graph, chart, diagram, or other graphic aid to solve each problem. Show your work.

1 A delivery truck leaves a store and travels in the following directions: 8 miles west, 10 miles south 2 miles east, and then 10 miles north. At the end of the route, how far is the truck from the store?

A 30 mi north of the store

B 30 mi south of the store

C 6 mi east of the store

D 6 mi west of the store

2 Cliff will use chicken wire to enclose part of his yard for a garden. He draws a picture to figure out how much fencing he needs. He wants the garden to be 8 ft wide and 14 ft long. How much chicke wire will he need?

F 44 ft

G 32 ft

H 30 ft

J 22 ft

3 The morning temperature in Nyack was 56° F. It rose 12° by noon. Then, a cold front came in and the temperature dropped 23° by 6:00 P.M. What was the temperature in Nyack at 6:00 P.M.?

A 47° F

B 45° F

C 42° F

D 33° F

4 Jason wants to build pigpens to house 3 pigs. Each pig needs a rectangular pen 10 ft wide by 20 ft long. The 3 pens will be side by side, each sharing its longest wall with another pen. How much fencing will Jason need?

F 140 ft

G 160 ft

H 580 ft

J 600 ft

Short-Response Question

5 A rectangle has an area of 60 in.². The length exceeds the width by 4 in. What are the dimensions of the rectangle? Explain how you arrived at your answer.

_____

_____

_____

_____

_____

Performance indicators: **8.CN.6, 8.PS.15, 8.M.1**

> **READY REFERENCE**
>
> **area** the number of square units that cover a surface

 Think About It

Measurement is part of everyday life. For example, geometry allows companies to determine the sizes of the packages and cans needed to hold the goods they produce. What are some everyday situations in which mathematics is used?

 Here's How

Kyle is helping to paint the outside of a playhouse for his younger sister. How many square feet will Kyle need to paint, including the area of the doors and windows?

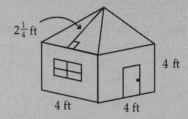

$2\frac{1}{4}$ ft

4 ft

4 ft   4 ft

The area that needs to be painted includes the four congruent square walls and the four congruent triangles that make up the roof.

Step 1   Make a table of the different faces to find the surface area.

Shape and Dimensions	How Many?	Total Area
Square: 4 ft by 4 ft	4	$4\,(4 \cdot 4) =$ _____
Triangle: b (base) $= 4$ ft, h (height) $= 2\frac{1}{4}$ ft	4	$4\left(\frac{1}{2} \cdot 4 \cdot 2\frac{1}{4}\right) =$ _____

Step 2   Add the areas.

_____ + _____ = _____

The total surface area is _____ ft²

Practice

Show your work.

1 A foot race covers a 42.2 km distance through the streets of a city, followed by a 400-m lap around a stadium. What is the total distance of the race in meters?

_____

2 Joe needs to add 3 in. of topsoil to a garden area 12 ft by 3 ft. How many cubic feet of topsoil will he need?

_____

3 Leticia is putting a box measuring 2 in. by 3 in. by 3 in. inside a gift box that is a 4 in. cube. How much space is left inside the gift box for packing material?

A 36 in.³

C 42 in.³

B 39 in.³

D 46 in.³

4 The perimeter of a rectangular picture frame is 48 in. The width is 10 in. What is the length?

F 28 in.

H 14 in.

G 19 in.

J 12 in.

5 The Farleys left home at 7:00 A.M. and drove directly to their vacation home 240 miles away. They arrived at 11:00 A.M. What was their average speed?

A 50 mph

C 70 mph

B 60 mph

D 80 mph

6 Carl is fencing off a 5 ft by 10 ft rectangular area of his back yard for a vegetable garden. The new fence will share one of its longer sides with the existing fence. How much fencing material will Carl need for his garden?

F 15 ft

H 25 ft

G 20 ft

J 30 ft

7 Shane is 6 ft tall and casts a shadow 17 ft long. At the same time, a nearby tree casts a shadow 102 ft long. What is the height of the tree?

A 17 ft

C 36 ft

B 25 ft

D 38 ft

8 A box of cereal has the dimensions 2 in. by 7 in. by 10 in. Ignoring overlap, how much cardboard was used to make the box?

F 208 in.²

H 140 in.²

G 168 in.²

J 108 in.²

Short-Response Question

9 Candace wants to cover the curved side of a can with paper and use it for a pencil holder. The can has a circumference of 8 cm and a height of 15 cm. What is the area of the surface she wants to cover?

_____

_____

_____

> **READY REFERENCE**
> **scale factor** the ratio of corresponding side lengths

Think About It

Ratios or proportions are used to make scale drawings. In order for the drawing to be accurate and fit on a sheet of paper, you must consider the scale possible for both the length and width.

Here's How

Reduce measurements to fit a small sheet of paper.

Suppose you want to construct a scale drawing of a house. The house measures 40 ft by 50 ft. What scale would allow you to draw it on a 6 in. by 9 in. sheet of paper?

Largest scale for width to fit $= \frac{\text{actual width}}{\text{paper width}} = \frac{40 \text{ ft}}{6 \text{ in.}} = \frac{6.667 \text{ ft}}{1 \text{ in.}} = 6.667 \text{ ft} : 1 \text{ in.}$

Largest scale for length to fit $= \frac{\text{actual length}}{\text{paper length}} = \frac{50 \text{ ft}}{9 \text{ in.}} = \frac{5.556 \text{ ft}}{1 \text{ in.}} = 5.556 \text{ ft} : 1 \text{ in.}$

When reducing to fit on the page, choose the greater of the two scales: _____

Enlarge measurements to fit on a large sheet of paper.

Suppose you want to make a scale drawing of a Booster badge that is 1.5 in. wide and 2 in. tall. What scale would allow you to draw it on a $8\frac{1}{2}$ in. by 11 in. sheet of paper?

Largest scale for length to fit $= \frac{\text{paper length}}{\text{actual length}} = \frac{11 \text{ in.}}{2 \text{ in.}} = \frac{5.5 \text{ in.}}{1 \text{ in.}} = 5.5 \text{ in.} : 1 \text{ in.}$

Largest scale for width to fit $= \frac{\text{paper width}}{\text{actual width}} = \frac{8.5 \text{ in.}}{1.5 \text{ in.}} = \frac{5.667 \text{ in.}}{1 \text{ in.}} = 5.667 \text{ in.} : 1 \text{ in.}$

When enlarging to fit on the page, choose the smaller scale: _____.

Practice

1 Measure the picture above. What are its length and width in inches to the nearest $\frac{1}{4}$ inch?

2 What scale would allow you to draw the picture on an $8\frac{1}{2}$ in. by 11 in. sheet of paper? Round to the nearest tenth.

_____

_____

3 A giraffe can be as tall as 18 ft. Find the maximum scale you can use for a model giraffe if it must fit in a 6-in.-tall zoo diorama.

A 3 ft : 1 in.

C 9 ft : 1 in.

B 6 ft. : 1 in.

D 3 in. : 1 ft

4 Find the maximum scale you can use for a model giraffe if it must fit in a room with a 9-ft ceiling.

F 2 ft : 1 in.

H 2 ft : 1 ft

G 3 ft : 1 in.

J 9 ft : 1 ft

5 Find the maximum scale you can use for a model giraffe if it must fit in a 2-ft-tall toy box.

A 4 ft : 1 ft

B 9 ft : 1 ft

C 9 ft : 2 ft

D 18 ft : 1 ft

6 Find the maximum scale you can use for a model giraffe if it must fit in an 8-ft-tall crate.

F 9 ft : 1 in. or 2.25 ft : 0.5 in.

G 9 ft : 1 ft or 2.25 ft : 1 in.

H 9 ft : 2 ft or 2.25 ft : 1 in.

J 9 ft : 4 ft or 2.25 ft : 1 ft

Short-Response Question

7 The figure at the right is a sketch of one side of a cabin. The actual dimensions of the cabin are listed below. Using a scale of 1 grid length : 2 ft, make a scale drawing of the front of the cabin on the grid provided.

Actual Measurements: Cabin width: 24 ft, Cabin height: 10 ft, Door width: 4 ft, Door height: 7 ft, Window width: 6 ft, Window height: 5 ft, Roof height: 8 ft.

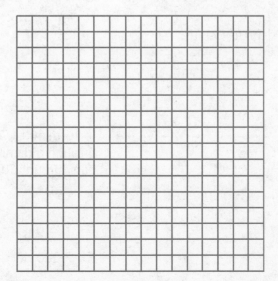

Directions

Use a separate sheet of paper to show your work.

1 If Jeremy can ride his bike 3.4 miles in a half hour, how far can he ride in 2 hours?

A 6.8 mi

B 13.6 mi

C 17 mi

D 29 mi

2 The Hudson River is 315 miles long. What is its length in feet?

F 1,575,000 ft

G 1,638,000 ft

H 1,663,200 ft

J 16,632,000 ft

3 From street level to the tip of its mast, the Empire State Building is 381 meters high. What is its height in centimeters?

A 38,100 cm

B 190,500 cm

C 381,000 cm

D 762,000 cm

4 Convert 100° Fahrenheit to degrees Celsius.

F 37.78°C

G 38°C

H 132.18°C

J 295.2°C

5 Convert −19° Celsius to degrees Fahrenheit.

A 23.4°F

B 17.445°F

C 9.2°F

D −2.2°F

6 Once an oven is turned on, it heats at a rate of 15°F every 2 minutes. How much hotter will the oven be in 30 minutes?

F 200°F

G 215°F

H 225°F

J 240°F

7 At sea level, sound travels at a speed of 1,116 ft per second. What is the speed in miles per hour? Round to the nearest tenth.

A 4,027,600 mph

B 760.9 mph

C 660 mph

D 12.682 mph

8 A scientist is studying the effects of temperature and pressure. The temperature in a chamber was 12°. It rose 15°, fell 37°, and then rose 5°. What is the current temperature in the chamber?

F −7°

G −5°

H 5°

J 17°

9 In 15 minutes, 1,875 gallons of water passes through a dam. How many gallons of water pass through the dam in 1 minute?

A 12.5 gal

B 125 gal

C 7,000 gal

D 7,500 gal

 Measuring Up® to the New York State Learning Standards

Use a picture, graph, chart, diagram, or other graphic aid to answer questions 10–11.

10 Eric is putting posts along a fence line. The ground is rocky, so he cannot space the posts evenly. Post A is put at the beginning of the fence line. Post B is 5 feet east of A. Post C is 8 feet east of B. Post D is 7 feet east of C. Post E is 10 feet east of D. How far is Post E from A?

    F 5 ft

    G 15 ft

    H 24 ft

    J 30 ft

11 A rectangular parking lot has an area of 510 m². The width exceeds the length by 13 m. What are the dimensions of the parking lot?

    A 31 m × 18 m

    B 30 m × 17 m

    C 28 m × 15 m

    D 25 m × 12 m

12 The volume of a cube is 216 cm³. What is the length and width of each face?

    F 6 cm × 6 cm

    G 8 cm × 8 cm

    H 10.5 cm × 10.5 cm

    J 14.696 cm × 14.696 cm

13 A hummingbird can beat its wings 50–200 times per second. If one hummingbird beats its wings at a rate of 161 times per second, how many times will it beat its wings in $\frac{1}{4}$ hour?

    A 2,415

    B 14,490

    C 144,900

    D 2,415,000

14 Miyoshi's grandfather's house is 96 miles by highway from his apartment. The speed limit is 65 mph. If Miyoshi's father drives 5 miles per hour under the speed limit, how long will the drive take?

    F 1.476 hours

    G 1.5 hours

    H 1.579 hours

    J 1.6 hours

15 There are 13 homes on one side of Jarod's street. Each home has a front yard 50 feet wide. If his street is twice as long as the combined width of all the yards, how many feet long is the street?

    A 400

    B 700

    C 900

    D 1,300

16 A gray whale can be 46 ft long. Find the maximum scale you can use for a toy whale if it must fit in an 11-in.-long cardboard box.

    F 4 ft : 1 in.

    G 50.18 in. : 1 in.

    H 5 ft. : 1 in.

    J 5 ft. : 1 ft

17 The *Saturn V* rocket was 111-m-tall with a 10-m diameter. Find the maximum scale you can use for drawing a *Saturn V* on an $8\frac{1}{2}$ by 11 in. sheet of paper.

    A 10.09 m : 1 in.

    B 10 m : 1 in.

    C 1.176 m : 1 in.

    D 1 m : 1 in.

18 A rectangular picture measuring 8 in. by 10 in. is going to be matted and framed. The matting is $\frac{3}{4}$ in. wide and the frame is an additional $\frac{3}{4}$ in. wide.

Part A Draw a sketch of the picture, matting, and frame.

Part B Find the area of the picture and of the picture once the matting has been added.

Area of the picture is 8 in. • _____ = _____

_____

_____

Part C Find the perimeter of the frame and the area of the framed picture.

_____

_____

_____

19 Sean and Michelle live on the same street. The video store where they both work is located between their houses. It takes Sean 10 minutes to walk from his house to the video store. Walking at the same rate, it takes Michelle twice as long as Sean to walk to the video store.

Part A Michelle lives $\frac{1}{2}$ mi from the video store. How far does Sean live from the video store?

_____

_____

_____

_____

Part B How long will it take Sean to walk to the video store, go to Michelle's house, return to the video store, and then go home? You may draw a diagram to help you solve the problem.

_____

_____

Lesson PM1 — Adding and Subtracting Monomials with Exponents of One

Performance Indicators: **7.A.2**

READY REFERENCE
monomial a number, a variable, or a product of numbers and variables

---

⚷ Remember This?

To add monomials with like variables, add just the numbers, the variables remain the same: $2xy + 4xy = 6xy$.
To subtract monomials with like variables, subtract just the numbers: $19bc - (-3bc) = 22bc$.

⚷ Practice

For each question, choose the correct answer from the four choices given.

1 $24ab + 37ab =$

  A $71ab$ **C** $51ab$

  B $61ab$ **D** $41ab$

2 $16xy - 19xy =$

  F $35xy$ **H** $3xy$

  G $32xy$ **J** $-3xy$

3 $12m + 26mn - 19mn =$

  A $38m - 45n$ **C** $19m + 45mn$

  B $16mn$ **D** $12m + 7mn$

4 $47bc - 29bc + 19bc =$

  F $37bc$ **H** $37bc + 19c$

  G $39bc$ **J** $39bc - 19b$

5 $1.021ab + 8.16ab =$

  A $9.181ab$

  B $9.037ab$

  C $9.0181ab$

  D $9.008ab$

6 $6a + 12a + 18b - (-b) + 14cd =$

  F $12a + 17b + 14cd$

  G $18a + 17b + 14cd$

  H $18a + 19b + 14cd$

  J $37ab + 14cd$

7 $27x + 19y - 47y + 8yz - 12yz =$

  A $27x - 28y - 4yz$

  B $27x + 28y + 4yz$

  C $27x - 63y - 4yz$

  D $27x + 28y - 20yz$

8 $a + 3a + 4a + 5b - 2b + c + 8c + 2cd$

  F $8a + 3b + 9c + 2cd$

  G $8a + 7b + 9c + 2cd$

  H $7a + 7b + 8c + 2cd$

  J $7a - 7b + 8c + 2cd$

Performance indicators: **7.A.3**

> **READY REFERENCE**
> **polynomial** an algebraic expression containing one or more monomials

🗝 Remember This?

> Any algebraic expression that can be written as the sum or difference of two or more monomials is a polynomial. Polynomials can be arranged in ascending or descending order by finding the powers common to both expressions. A monomial is a number, a variable, or a product of numbers and variables. A monomial cannot have a variable in the denominator of a fraction or a variable with a radical sign.

🗝 Practice

1 Which of the following is a monomial?

A $19x$

B $yz - 32$

C $a + b$

D $\frac{2x}{13y}$

2 Which of the following is a polynomial?

F $\sqrt{x}$

G $32x^2y + 19y$

H $x + \frac{2}{y}$

J $\frac{9}{d^3}$

3 $9x - 14yz$ is a polynomial because

A the second monomial can be subtracted from the first.

B the expression is the difference between two monomials.

C the result is a negative number.

D the expression contains the integers 9 and 14.

4 Which of the following is a polynomial?

F $37cd + 106e^2$

G $3bc - \frac{2}{cd}$

H $27bc + \sqrt{b} - 12cd$

J $23c^2 + \frac{19}{b}$

5 Which of the following is a polynomial?

A $\frac{2}{3}ab^4 - \sqrt{x}$

B $\frac{7}{16}x^2 - \frac{3}{x}$

C $\frac{17}{6}x^2 - \frac{8}{x^2}$

D $\frac{1}{2}ab^4 - ab$

6 Which of the following is a polynomial?

F $4r^2 + 19r - 37$

G $1.234st - \frac{1.134}{st} + 2.134s^2$

H $0.012s + 1.23s - \sqrt{s}$

J $2rst - \frac{14}{19rst^2}$

7 Which polynomial is arranged so that the powers of y are in ascending order?

A $7y - 5y^2 - 4y$

B $21y + 28y^4 + 43y^3$

C $6y - 63y^2 - 64y^5$

D $3y + 28y^2 - 20y$

8 Which polynomial is arranged so that the powers of x are in descending order?

F $8x^{12} + 3x^{15} + 2x^9$

G $18x^6 + 7x^3 + 4x$

H $5x + 17x^3 + 84x^2$

J $x - 7x^3 + 8x^2$

Performance indicators: **7.A.4**

READY REFERENCE
combine terms to add or subtract terms that are identical
distributive property $a(b + c) = ab + ac$ and $a(b - c) = ab - ac$

Remember This?

Three possible methods of solving multi-step equations are:

Combine like terms	Use the distributive property	Move variables to one side of the equation
$1x + 2x = 6$ $3x = 6$ $x = 2$	$2(x + 3x) = 24$ $2x + 6x = 24$ $8x = 24$ $x = 3$	$22 + 12x = x$ $22 + 12x - 12x = x - 12x$ $22 = -11x$ $-2 = x$

Practice

Solve each equation below.

1 $12a - 9a = 132$

A $a = 44$ **C** $a = 6.6$

B $a = 33$ **D** $a = 1.5238095$

2 $3(4b - 2b) = 54$

F $b = 3.857$ **H** $b = 9$

G $b = 6$ **J** $b = 11\frac{1}{3}$

3 $18x - 14 = 11x + 7$

A $x = 2$ **C** $x = 5$

B $x = 3$ **D** $x = 7$

4 $3(2b + 14) = 7b - 14$

F $b = 56$ **H** $b = -14$

G $b = 0$ **J** $b = -28$

5 $2y - 8 = 8y - 12$

A $y = 10$ **C** $y = 2$

B $y = 4$ **D** $y = \frac{2}{3}$

6 $5(2a + 3) = 2(3a + 11)$

F $a = 2$ **H** $a = 1.75$

G $a = 1.8$ **J** $a = 1.5$

7 $6(x - 2) = 2x \cdot 2$

A $x = 1$ **C** $x = 6$

B $x = 3$ **D** $x = 8$

8 $2(x + 3) = \frac{1}{3} x - 9$

F $x = -18$ **H** $x = 3$

G $x = -9$ **J** $x = 9$

Performance indicators: **7.A.7**

READY REFERENCE
representation a graphic model of a mathematical idea, such as a drawing, diagram, or graph
pattern a sequence of items or numbers that occur in a certain order

 Remember This?

Numbers or items may occur in a sequence, forming a pattern. The numbers or items may be listed in a table, which can show how groups of items change as the pattern continues.

An equation with two variables, such as $y = 2x + 1$, also indicates a pattern. By replacing the value of x with various numbers, you can find corresponding values of y. Then you can graph each ordered pair (x, y) as points. If the equation is a linear equation, the points can be connected to form a straight line.

Practice

1 Which representation models the pattern shown in the following table?

white circles	shaded circles
2	0
3	1
4	2
5	3

2 The table below shows some ordered pairs that satisfy the equation $y = x - 2$. Which graph represents the pattern as shown by the equation.

x	y
2	0
3	1
4	2
5	3

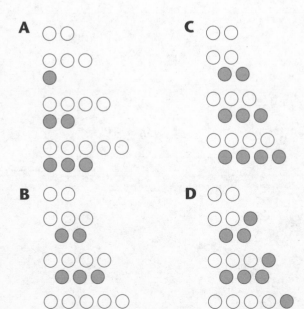

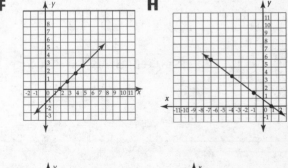

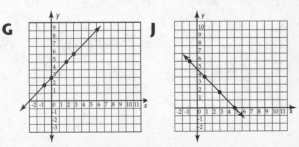

🔑 Remember This?

You can use algebra to write a rule for the pattern of a sequence of numbers. For example, one pattern that can be applied to the sequence 2, 4, 6, 8,... relates the value of a term to its place in the sequence: 1st term = 2(1), 2nd term = 2(2), 3rdt term = 2(3), 4th term = 2(4). If the pattern continues, the value of the *n*th term is 2(*n*). So, an algebraic rule for this sequence is 2*n*, where *n* represents the place number of a term.

🔑 Practice

Use this sequece to answer questions 1–3.

11, 22, 33, 44,...

1 If the pattern continues, what is the next term of the sequence? _____

2 If the pattern continues, what is a rule for the *n*th term of the sequence? _____

3 Use the rule to find the 20th term of the sequence. _____

4 Give the rule for the sequence 7, 13, 19, 25. _____

5 What are the first four terms in the sequence described by the rule 7*n* − 2? _____

6 What are the first four terms in the sequence described by the rule 3*n* + 2? _____

7 Find the next term in the sequence 3, 1, 75, 375....

   A 387   **B** 475   **C** 1,125   **D** 1,875

8 Which expression represents the sequence 13, 16, 19, 22...?

   F 4*n* − 1   **G** *n* + 2   **H** 3*n*   **J** 3*n* + 10

Performance indicators: **7.A.9**

READY REFERENCE

polygon a closed plane figure with sides that are line segments

quadrilateral a closed plane figure with four sides and four angles whose
  measures total 360°

🔑 **Remember This?**

A polygon has three or more sides. An *n*-gon is a polygon with *n* sides. You can find a pattern and write a rule for the sum of the measure of the interior angles of a polygon.

🔑 **Practice**

Polygon	Number of Sides	Number of Triangles that Form the polygon	Sum of the Angle Measures
Triangle	3		$1 \cdot 180° =$
Quadrilateral	4		$2 \cdot 180° =$
Pentagon	5		$3 \cdot 180° =$
Hexagon	6		$4 \cdot 180° =$
Heptagon	7		$5 \cdot 180° =$
Octagon	8		$6 \cdot 180° =$

1 Look at the figures below. Count the number of triangles that can be drawn with diagonals from one vertex. Use this information to fill in the third column in the chart.

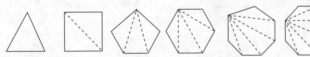

2 What is the sum of the measures of the interior angles for each figure? Use this information to fill in the fourth column of the chart.

3 If a polygon has *n* sides, which expression shows the number of triangles that can be formed in the polygon?

A $2n - 2$ **B** $2n$ **C** $n + 2$ **D** $n - 2$

4 Which expression is the rule for determining the sum of the interior angle measurements of an *n*-gon with *x*-sides?

F $n \cdot 90°$ **G** $(n - 2)180°$ **H** $n \cdot 180°$ **J** $(n - 2)360°$

5 What is the sum of the interior angle measurements of a nonagon, or 9-sided polygon?

A $1,080°$ **B** $1,260°$ **C** $1,440°$ **D** $1,620°$

Performance indicators: **7.A.10**

READY REFERENCE

x	$y = x + 3$	y
-1	$y = -1 + 3$	2
0	$y = 0 + 3$	3
1	$y = 1 + 3$	4
2	$y = 2 + 3$	5
3	$y = 3 + 3$	6
4	$y = 4 + 3$	7

An equation can represent a functional relationship. You can use the numbers in a table of values to write an equation that expresses the functional relationship. The equation $y = x + 3$ corresponds to the values for x and y as shown in the table to the right.

Practice

For questions 1–2, use the tables to determine the appropriate equation.

1 **A** $y = x + 3$

B $y = x \cdot 3$

C $y = x - 3$

D $y = x \div 3$

x	y
2	5
3	6
4	7
5	8

2 **F** $y = 3x$

G $y = x + 3$

H $y = -x - 3$

J $y = x - 3$

x	y
-3	0
-4	1
-5	2
-6	3

3 Which equation corresponds to the table of values shown below?

A $y = x \div 2$

B $y = x \cdot 2$

C $y = (x - 2) + 1$

D $y = (x \div 3) + 2$

x	y
-4	-2
-2	-1
0	0
2	1
4	2

4 Which algebraic pattern is represented by the chart below?

Sales at the Corner Book Shoppe

	History Books Sold(x)	Mystery Books Sold(y)
Monday	3	9
Tuesday	4	12
Wednesday	5	15
Thursday	6	18

F $y = x + 6$ **H** $y = 3x + 2$

G $y = 3x$ **J** $3y = x$

5 Which equation corresponds to the table of values shown below?

A $y = x^3$

B $y = \dfrac{x + 2}{3}$

C $y = 3 \div (x^2 + 2)$

D $y = x^2 + 2$

x	y
-5	-1
-2	0
1	1
4	2
7	3

6 Which equation corresponds to the table of values shown below?

F $y = (x - 1) \div 2$

G $y = \dfrac{x - 1}{2}$

H $y = 1.5\,(x - 1)$

J $y = 2(x - 1)$

x	y
-1	-4
0	-2
1	0
2	2
3	4

> **READY REFERENCE**
> **right triangle** a triangle that includes a right angle

🔑 Remember This?

A right triangle has one right angle, or one angle that measures 90°. The sides that form the right angle are the legs of the right triangle. The side opposite the right angle is the hypotenuse.

🔑 Practice

Use the figures below to answer questions 1–6.

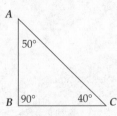

Figure 1

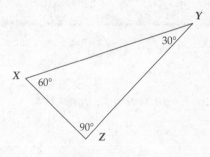

Figure 2

1 Which angle makes Figure 1 a right triangle?

   A ∠A   **C** ∠C

   B ∠B   **D** ∠B and ∠C

2 Which angle makes Figure 2 a right triangle?

   F ∠Z   **H** ∠X

   G ∠Y   **J** ∠X and ∠Z

3 In Figure 1, which sides are the legs of the right triangle?

   A $\overline{AB}$ and $\overline{AC}$

   B $\overline{AB}$ and $\overline{BA}$

   C $\overline{BC}$ and $\overline{AC}$

   D $\overline{BC}$ and $\overline{AB}$

4 In Figure 2, which sides are the legs of the right triangle?

   F $\overline{XZ}$ and $\overline{XY}$

   G $\overline{YX}$ and $\overline{ZX}$

   H $\overline{XZ}$ and $\overline{YZ}$

   J $\overline{XY}$ and $\overline{XZ}$

5 In Figure 1, which side of the right triangle is the hypotenuse?

   A $\overline{AB}$ **C** $\overline{BC}$

   B $\overline{AC}$ **D** $\overline{BA}$

6 In Figure 2, which side of the right triangle is the hypotenuse?

   F $\overline{XZ}$ **H** $\overline{XY}$

   G $\overline{YZ}$ **J** $\overline{ZX}$

> **READY REFERENCE**
>
> **Pythagorean theorem** the relationship among the lengths of the three sides of a right triangle

🔑 Remember This?

The diagram shows a right triangle with a square with a square fitted to each of the sides. The sum of the areas of the squares on the legs of the triangle is the exact value of the area of the square on the hypottenuse. If a and b represent the lengths of the legs, and c represents the length of the hypotenuse, then $a^2 + b^2 = c^2$.

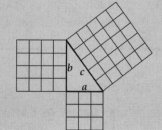

🔑 Practice

Use the figure to answer questions 1–6.

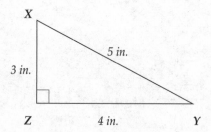

1 What is the square of the length of $\overline{XZ}$?

   A 6 in.   **C** 12 in.

   B 9 in.   **D** 15 in.

2 What is the square of the length of $\overline{ZY}$?

   F 4 in.   **H** 12 in.

   G 8 in.   **J** 16 in.

3 What is the sum of the squares of $\overline{XZ}$ and side $\overline{YZ}$?

   A 25 in.   **C** 20 in.

   B 24 in.   **D** 18 in.

4 Which side's length when squared is equal to the sum of the squares of the other two sides?

   F hypotenuse $\overline{XY}$ **H** leg $\overline{YX}$

   G leg $\overline{XZ}$ **J** leg $\overline{ZX}$

5 Which represents the length of the hypotenuse?

   A $\sqrt{5}$

   B $\sqrt{9}$

   C $\sqrt{25}$

   D $\sqrt{225}$

6 Which equation represents the relationship of the squares of the lengths of the right triangle's sides?

   F $(3 + 4)^2 = 5^2$

   G $(3 + 4)^2 = \sqrt{25}$

   H $3^2 + 4^2 = 5^2$

   J $3^2 + 4 = 5^2$

READY REFERENCE

Pythagorean theorem the relationship among the lengths of the three sides of a right triangle, leg² + leg² = hypotenuse²

Remember This?

When you know the lengths of any two sides of a right triangle, you can use the Pythagorean theorem to find the length of the third side;

example: The legs of a right triangle measure 5 cm and 12 cm. Find the length of the hypotenuse.

$$leg^2 + leg^2 = hypotenuse^2$$
$$5^2 + 12^2 = h^2$$
$$25 + 144 = h^2$$
$$169 = h^2$$
$$\sqrt{169} = \sqrt{h^2}$$
$$13 = h \qquad \text{So, the length of the hypotenuse is 13 cm.}$$

Practice

Use the Pythagorean theorem to find the unknown length in each right triangle in questions 1–2.

1 What is the length *n* in the figure below?

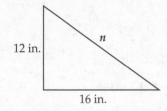

12 in.   *n*
16 in.

A *n* = 16 in. **C** *n* = 24 in.

B *n* = 20 in. **D** *n* = 40 in.

2 What is the length *n* in the figure below?

15 ft.   *n*
9 ft.

F *n* = 122 ft. **H** *n* = 12 ft

G *n* = 44 ft **J** *n* = 10 ft

3 The legs of a right triangle measure 6 ft. and 8 ft. Find the length of the hypotenuse.

A 8 ft

B 10 ft

C 14 ft

D 100 ft

4 The hypotenuse of a right triangle measures 17 m and one leg measures 15 m. Find the measure of the other leg.

F 8 m

H 32 m

G 64 m

J 128 m

🔑 Remember This?

If you know the lengths of the sides of a triangle, you can use the Pythagorean theorem to determine if it is a right triangle. The square of the length of the hypotenuse must equal the sum of the squares of the lengths of the other two side.

🔑 Practice

Use a calculator and the Pythagorean theorem to determine the answer to each question.

1 Which of the following measures describes the sides of a right triangle?

A 3 mi, 4 mi, 5 mi

B 4 mi, 5 mi, 6 mi

C 7 mi, 8 mi, 9 mi

D 9 mi, 10 mi, 11 mi

2 Which of the following measures describes the sides of a right triangle?

F 5 m, 11 m, 12 m

G 5 m, 12 m, 13 m

H 11 m, 12 m, 13 m

J 11 m, 13 m, 14 m

3 Which of the following measures describes the sides of a right triangle?

A 9 cm, 20 cm, 22 cm

B 9 cm, 25 cm, 30 cm

C 9 cm, 40 cm, 41 cm

D 9 cm, 45 cm, 48 cm

4 Which of the following measures describes the sides of a right triangle?

F 6 yd, 7 yd, 9 yd

G 6 yd, 8 yd, 10 yd

H 7 yd, 8 yd, 9 yd

J 8 yd, 10 yd, 12 yd

5 Which of the following measures describes the sides of a right triangle?

A 10 m, 14 m, 16 m

C 10 m, 20 m, 24 m

B 10 m, 18 m, 24 m

D 10 m, 24 m, 26 m

6 Which of the following measures describes the sides of a right triangle?

F 7 in., 24 in., 25 in.

G 7 in., 20 in., 22 in.

H 6 in., 18 in., 21 in.

J 5 in., 15 in., 20 in.

Measuring Up® to the New York State Learning Standards

READY REFERENCE

map scale a ratio that compares a unit of length to an actual distance, such as
1 inch = 10 miles

Remember This?

You can use a map scale to calculate actual distances from a map. For example, a map has a scale of
1 inch = 150 miles. What is the actual distance between two towns that are $2\frac{3}{8}$ inches apart on the map?

$$\frac{1}{150} = \frac{2.375}{x} \qquad 1 \cdot x = 150 \cdot 2.375 \qquad x = 356.25$$

The actual distance between the two towns is $356\frac{1}{4}$ miles.

Practice

For questions 1–2, use a map scale of 1 cm = 35 miles.

1 On a map, Potter Flats and Tansonville are
7 cm apart. What is the actual distance between
these two towns?

  A 70 miles   **C** 245 miles

  B 210 miles   **D** 325 miles

2 The actual distance between Tecumseh and Silver
Lake is 560 miles. How far apart would Tecumseh
and Silver Lake be on the map?

  F 11 cm   **H** 15 cm

  G 12 cm   **J** 16 cm

For questions 3–4, use a map scale of 1 inch = 200 miles.

3 On a map, Northwest College is $2\frac{3}{4}$ inches
from Empire City. What is the actual distance
between the college and Empire City?

  A 480 miles   **C** 575 miles

  B 550 miles   **D** 650 miles

4 The actual distance between two towns is
135 miles. How far apart would they be on
the map?

  F 0.675 inch   **H** 0.875 inch

  G 0.75 inch   **J** 1.15 inches

5 The table below shows ratios of centimeters to kilometers. What is the scale of the map it describes?

Size on map	3 cm	5 cm	7 cm	9 cm
Actual size	39 km	65 km	91 km	117 km

  A 1 cm = 3 km   **B** 1 cm = 9 km   **C** 1 cm = 13 km   **D** 1 cm = 39 km

Performance indicators: **7.M.5**

READY REFERENCE

rate a ratio comparing two different types of quantities

unit price the price of one unit, expressed as a rate with a denominator of 1

Remember This?

You can use proportions to find the unit price of an item. What is the unit price of an 18-oz box of cereal that costs $5.16?

Find the unit price by dividing the total cost by the number of units. Change dollars and cents to cents.	$\frac{516 \, cents}{18 \, oz} = ?$
Divide and round to the nearest penny.	$\frac{516 \, cents}{18 \, oz} = \$0.286 \rightarrow \$0.29$

The unit price for the cereal is about $0.29 per ounce.

Practice

1 A 12-oz bottle of grape juice costs $0.79. How can you express the unit price of the grape juice?

A $\frac{12 \, oz}{\$0.79}$

C $\frac{\$0.79}{12 \, oz}$

B $12 \, oz \times \$0.79$

D $12 \, oz \times \frac{\$0.79}{2}$

2 A 12-oz bottle of apple juice costs $1.13. What is the unit price of the apple juice? Round to the nearest cent.

F $0.07

H $0.12

G $0.09

J $0.23

3 Five pounds of ground beef costs $12.78. What is the unit price of the ground beef? Round to the nearest cent.

A $1.78

C $2.45

B $1.98

D $2.56

4 Duncan paid $2.07 to make 23 copies at a print shop. At this rate, how much would he pay to make 40 copies? Show your work.

F $3.60

H $4.14

G $4.07

J $4.44

5 The centerfielder for the New York Yankees made $1,150,000 to play baseball last season. If he played in 162 games, what was the unit cost to the Yankees per game? Round to the nearest cent.

> **READY REFERENCE**
> **unit price** the price of one unit, expressed as a rate with a denominator of 1

 Remember This?

You can use rate to compare the unit price of items. If one item costs $3.95 for 20 oz and another item costs $4.15 for 28 oz, which is the better buy?

$$\frac{\$3.95}{20 \text{ oz}} = \$0.1975 \rightarrow \$0.20 \text{ per oz}$$

$$\$0.15 < \$0.20$$

$$\frac{\$4.15}{28 \text{ oz}} = \$0.1482 \rightarrow \$0.15 \text{ per oz}$$

Compare the unit prices to find the better value: The better buy is the item that costs $4.15 for 28 oz.

 **Practice**

1 Today's supermarket ads feature four different specials on plums. Which store has the best unit price on plums?

Gordon's Food Store	Janet's Grocery Shop
Plums	Fresh Plums
2 lbs for $1.84	1 lb for $0.91
MegaFood	**Handy Foods**
Delicious Plums	Ripe Plums
3 lbs for $2.64	5 lbs for $4.30

A Gordon's Food Store **C** Janet's Grocery Stop

B MegaFood **D** Handy Foods

2 At an office supply store, Patricia has the choices shown below for purchasing envelopes. Which choice offers the lowest unit price?

F 700 envelopes for $36.89 **H** 1,500 envelopes for $45.52

G 950 envelopes for $37.65 **J** 2,000 envelopes for $78.11

3 Hideki wants to subscribe to the new monthly magazine *Hiking in America*. Which subscription offer has the lowest unit price per issue?

A 12 issues for $23.95 **C** 36 issues for $68.32

B 24 issues for $46.70 **D** 48 issues for $88.32

4 Mrs. Jackson paid $29.90 for 12 gallons of gasoline. Her neighbor, Mr. Costello, paid $2.47 a gallon at a different gas station. Who paid the lower unit price per gallon?

Performance indicators: **7.M.7**

READY REFERENCE
conversion rate a special ratio that compares the buying power of two currencies

Remember This?

The conversion rate of U.S. dollars to Russian rubles was 1 dollar: 28.34 rubles. How many rubles can be exchanged for $245?

$$\frac{1}{28.34} = \frac{245}{x} \qquad\qquad x = 245 \cdot 28.34 \qquad\qquad x = 6{,}943.3$$

245 U.S. dollars can be exchanged for 6,943.3 Russian rubles

Practice

Use the currency conversion table to find the answers to questions 1–4.

	British pound sterling	Canadian dollar	European Union euro	Japanese yen	U.S. dollar
1 British pound sterling		2.17	1.45	198.67	1.81
1 Canadian dollar	0.46		0.67	91.43	0.83
1 European Union euro	0.69	2.17		136.70	1.24
1 Japanese yen	0.005	0.001	0.007		0.009
1 U.S. dollar	0.55	1.20	0.80	109.96	

1 How many euros would it take to purchase an item worth 10 U.S. dollars?

A 5 **C** 8 **B** 6 **D** 10

2 Monique bought an automobile in France that cost 14,481.70 euros. About how much is this in U.S. dollars?

F 1,805 dollars **G** 18,000 dollars **H** 25,000 dollars **J** 501,000 dollars

3 A set of golf clubs at a Tokyo sporting goods store costs 38,000 Japanese yen. About how much is this in British pounds sterling?

A 190 pounds sterling **C** 380 pounds sterling **B** 270 pounds sterling **D** 525 pounds sterling

4 Joseph has 5,000 dollars in a savings account in the United States. If he moves his money to a bank in Montreal, about how much will his savings be worth in Canadian dollars?

F 3,900 Canadian dollars **H** 5,000 Canadian dollars

G 4,200 Canadian dollars **J** 6,000 Canadian dollars

Measuring Up® to the New York State Learning Standards

Directions

Use a separate sheet of paper to show your work.

1 Simplify $16w + 21w + 81x - (-2x) + 41yz$.

A $16w + 102x + 41yz$

B $37w + 79x + 41yz$

C $37w + 83x + 41yz$

D $37w + 124xyz$

2 Which of the following is a polynomial?

F $5x + \frac{1}{y}$

G $8x^2 - \frac{3}{2y} + 4$

H $7x^2 + 14x + 21$

J $\sqrt{2x} + 2$

3 Which value of x satisfies the following equation?
$3(x + 5) = \frac{1}{2}x - 5$

A $x = -8\frac{1}{2}$

B $x = -8$

C $x = 8$

D $x = 8\frac{1}{2}$

4 What algebraic pattern is represented by the values in the function table below?

x	y
0	0
1	2
2	4
3	6

F $y = x \bullet 3$

G $y = \frac{x + 6}{2}$

H $y = \frac{1}{3}x \bullet 6$

J $y = x \div -3$

5 What is the sum of the measures of the angles in this polygon?

A $540°$

B $360°$

C $270°$

D $180°$

6 Which side of the right triangle is the hypotenuse?

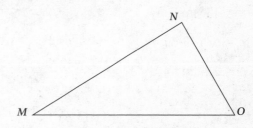

F $\overline{MO}$

G $\overline{NO}$

H $\overline{ON}$

J $\overline{MN}$

Use the figure below to answer question 7.

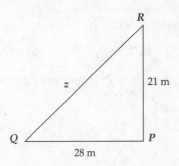

7 Which equation can be used to find the length of $\overline{QR}$?

A $21^2 + 28^2 = z^2$

B $21^2 + 28 = z^2$

C $28 + 21^2 = z$

D $28^2 + 21 = z^2$

8 What is the length n in the figure below?

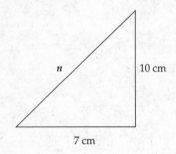

7 cm

10 cm

n

F $n = 11$ cm

G $n = \sqrt{149}$ cm

H $n = 12$ cm

J $n = \sqrt{170}$ cm

Use a calculator and the Pythagorean theorem to answer questions 9–10.

9 Which of the following measures describes the sides of a right triangle?

A 65 ft, 72 ft, 97 ft

B 65 ft, 70 ft, 90 ft

C 60 ft, 62 ft, 64 ft

D 50 ft, 50 ft, 55 ft

10 Which of the following measures describes the sides of a right triangle?

F 6 in., 7 in., 9 in.

G 6 in., 6 in., 8 in.

H 7 in., 6 in., 9 in.

J 9 in., 12 in., 15 in.

For question 11, use a map scale of 1 cm = 18 miles.

11 On a map, Kingston and Huron are 6.3 cm apart. What is the actual distance between these two towns?

A 84 miles

B 111.3 miles

C 113.4 miles

D 134.11 miles

12 A $1\frac{1}{2}$-pound package of chicken costs $2.24. What is the unit price of the chicken? Round to the nearest cent.

F $1.49

G $1.48

H $1.12

J $1.00

13 Examine the right triangular prism below.

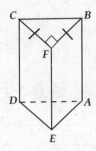

Part A   Identify the type and number of the polygons that make up the triangular prism.

_____

Part B   Name all the polygons that are congruent.

_____

_____

Part C   What is the sum of the angles in each of the polygons?

_____

_____

Part D   Suppose you drew a line from point *F* to bisect ∠*CFB*, forming 2 congruent polygons. What two polygons would be formed?

_____

14 Janeese keeps a record of the distance she walks each day. On Sunday, she walked 1 mile. Each day after that, she walked 0.2 miles farther than the day before.

Part A Complete the table below to show the distance Janeese walked each day and the total distance she walked for the week.

Day	Sun.	Mon.	Tues.	Wed.	Thurs.	Fri.	Sat.
Distance walked each day (miles)	1	1.2	1.4				
Total walked for the week (miles)	1	2.2	3.6				

Part B Use the numbers 1 through 7 for the days of the week (Sunday through Saturday) and graph the total distance Janeese walked by the end of each day as shown in the table.

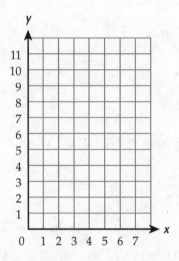

Tips for Taking the Test

When you take a mathematics test, you can show yourself, your family, and your teachers what you know about mathematics. Here are some Tips for Taking Tests that that will help you do your best job with the problems.

Listen Be sure you've listened to any directions from those giving the test.
Scan Look quickly over the entire test before you begin.
Read Read directions carefully. Read each test item carefully as you work.
Check Go back over the test to make sure you did your best.

 ## MULTIPLE–CHOICE QUESTIONS

Multiple-Choice Questions will each have several choices for answers. Each set of four answers is labeled A, B, C, D or F, G, H, J.

Choose your answers only from those given for the specific question. Here are easy things that will help you:

1. Read the test item very carefully. Reading it more than once can be helpful.
2. Decide what you need to do to find a solution.
3. Pick out the mathematical details that will help you find a solution.
4. Look at the answers and eliminate any that you know for sure are wrong.
5. Solve the problem that will provide the answer.
6. Check your work.
7. Choose the answer that matches your solution.

SHORT-RESPONSE AND EXTENDED-RESPONSE QUESTIONS

Short-Response Questions ask you to do more than solve a problem. You may be asked to SHOW HOW you solved the problem and EXPLAIN the answer. You may have to DRAW a picture, diagram, table, or other graphic to illustrate your answer.

Extended-Response Questions are longer and may have more than one step. These kinds of questions take more thought and more time to complete.

1. Read response questions carefully. Think about what you are asked.
2. Decide what you must do to answer the question or solve the problem.
3. Answer the question, solve the problem, and show your work.
4. Check to make sure your answer matches what you were asked and your work is correct.
5. Look back at the response question; make sure you have answered all the parts.

Glossary

A

additive property add equal quantities to equals and the sums are equal; example: $8 + 6 = 8 + 6$

adjacent angles angles with the same vertex and a common side

algebraic expression a variable by itself, or a combination of variables, numbers, and operations

angle a figure formed by two rays that have a common endpoint

alternate interior angles angles on opposite sides of the transversal that are between parallel lines

alternate exterior angles the angles on opposite sides of the transversal that are outside the parallel lines

area the number of square units that cover a surface

B

base the repeated number in a power; in the expression 3^2, 3 is base

binomial a polynomial with exactly two terms

C

Celsius a scale for measuring temperature. On the Celsius scale, water boils at 100° and freezes at 0°.

combine terms to add or subtract terms that are identical

common factor an expression that is a factor of two or more expressions

complementary angles two angles whose measures add up to 90°

congruent figures that have the same shape and the same size; the symbol $\cong$ means *is congruent to*

coversion rate a special ratio that compares the buying power of currencies

coordinate plane a plane divided into four quadrants defined by the x-axis and the y-axis

corresponding angles angles with equal measure that lie on the same side of the transversal and the same side of each parallel line

cross products in a proportion, where b and $d \neq 0$ if $\frac{a}{b} = \frac{c}{d}$, then $ad = bc$

D

dependent variables the variable in a relation whose value depends on the values of the independent variable

dilation a transformation that changes the size of a figure to produce an image that is similar to the original figure

distributive property $a(b + c) = ab + ac$ and $a(b - c) = ab - ac$

division property divide equal quantities by equals and the quotients are equal; example: $\frac{6}{5} = \frac{6}{5}$

domain the set of all first coordinates or x values from the ordered pairs in a relation

E

equation a statement that two expressions are equal

 Measuring Up® to the New York State Learning Standards

exponent a number that expresses how many times a base is used as a factor; example: $6 \cdot 6 \; 6 \cdot 6 = 6^4$. The base is 6 and the exponent is 4. So $6^4 = 6 \cdot 6 \cdot 6 \cdot 6 = 1{,}296$

exterior angle the angle formed by one side of the polygon and the extension of the adjaent side; the sum of the exterior angles of all convex polygons is 360°

F

factor an expression that divides into another expression with no remainder

Fahrenheit a scale for measuring temperature. On the Fahrenheit scale, water boils at 212° and freezes at 32°

function a relation in which each value of an independent variable is associated with only one value of the dependent variable

G

greatest common factor (GCF) the greatest expression that is a factor of two or more expressions

I

independent variable the variable in a relation whose value is subject to choice

inequality a comparison of two expressions that use uses one of the symbols $<\, .\, >\, ,\, \leq\, ,\, \geq\, ,$ or $\neq$.

interior angle the angle formed by two adjacent sides of the polygon; the sum of the interior angles in a triangle is 180° and in general is $(n-2)180°$, where n is the number of sides of the polygon

irrational number a number that cannot be written as a simple fraction; it is an infinite and non-repeating decimal

L

linear equation an equation whose graph is a straight line; example: $y = 2x - 3$

linear relationship an equation that has variables raised only to the first power, such as $y = 3x - 8$. The equation describes a constant rate of change.

M

map scale a ratio that compares a unit of length to an actual distance, such as 1 inch = 10 miles

monomial a number, a variable, or a product of numbers and variables

multiplicative property multiply equal quantities by equals and the properties are equal; example: $7(5) = 7(5)$

N

nonlinear relationship an equation that has one or more variables raised to a power other than 1, such as $y = 4 \times 2 + 10$; the equation does not have a constant rate of change, its graph is of a curve

number line a diagram that shows numbers, in order, on a line

O

ordered pair a point in the coordinate plane where the first value corresponds to the x value and the second to the y: example: $(3, -2)$

P

parallel lines lines in the same plane that always remain the same distance apart

pattern a sequence of items or numbers that occur in a certain order

percent a ratio that compares a number to 100

percent of change the ratio of the amount of change to the original amount; P = amount of change/original amount

pi π, the ratio of the circumference of a circle to its diameter

polygon a closed plane figure with sides that are line segments

polynomial an algebraic expression containing one or more monomials

power any expression written in exponential form, such as 3^2 or a^3

product of powers for any real number a and positive integers m and n: $a^m \cdot a^n = a^{m + n}$

profit the difference between money earned (income) and expenses

proportion an equation showing that two ratios are equal

Pythagorean theorem the sum of the squares of the legs of a right triangle is equal to the square of the hypotenuse

Q

quadratic equation an equation in the form of $y = ax^2 + bx + c$, where a, b, and c are real numbers; example: $y = 2x^2 - 3x + 5$

quadrilateral closed plane figure with four sides and four angles that total 360°

quotient of powers for any nonzero number a and whole numbers m and n: $\frac{a^m}{a^n} = a^{m - n}$

R

range the set of all second coordinates or y values from the ordered pairs in a relation

rate a ratio comparing two different types of quantities, such as miles to hours or feet to seconds

ratio the comparison of two numbers by division

reflection a transformation that produces the mirror image of a geometric figure

relation a set of ordered pairs

representation a graphic model of a mathematical idea, such as a drawing, diagram, or graph

right triangle a triangle that includes a right angle

rotation a transformation in which a figure pivots or turns around a fixed point or a line

S

scale a ratio between two sets of measurements

scale factor the ratio of corresponding side lengths

similar having the same shape but not necessarily the same size

simple interest interest calculated on the principal, or the initial amount of money invested or borrowed

simplest form a fraction for which the numerator and denominator cannot be divided by a common number greater than 1

solution a value that can be substituted for a variable to make an equation true

straight angle an angle formed by two opposing rays

subtraction property subtract equals from equals and the differences are equal; example: $9 - 4 = 9 - 4$

supplementary angles two angles whose measures add up to 180°

symmetry a figure has a line of symmetry when the part of the figure on one side of the line is the mirror image, or reflection, of the part on the other side

T

transformation an operation on a geometric figure that produces an image that differs from the original figure in size, shape, or position

translation a transformation that moves a geometric figure by sliding each of the points the same distance in the same direction

transversal a line that intersects two or more other lines

trinomial the sum of three monomials

U

unit price the price of one unit, expressed as a rate with a denominator of 1

V

vertex the point at which two lines, line segments, or rays meet to form an angle

vertical angles angles with equal measure that lie on opposite sides of two intersecting lines

Z

zero as an exponent for any non-zero number a, $a^0 = 1$

Measuring Up® to the New York State Learning Standards